Dr. Hilliard Speaks to Women of All Ages

▶ "Everything th[at] ing love-making, ful, has happened before. . . . There is enormous therapeutic value in a wife's learning that her problem is not unique and insoluble, but universal and solved every day."

▶ " 'I'm not that kind of girl,' they explain to me. This is outrageous nonsense. Except for a statistical handful who have abnormally low metabolisms, everybody is that kind of girl."

▶ "I believe fatigue to be the greatest enemy a woman ever faces and, tragically enough, the one she is least likely to recognize."

▶ "The menopause? It's women's greatest blessing. . . . Generations of panicky women have spawned enough untruths about the menopause to panic the next five generations."

These sample quotations show that in this book, as in her private office, Dr. Hilliard has brought understanding to women through warm and wise discussion. *A Woman Doctor Looks at Love and Life* may be obtained in a more permanent binding in its Doubleday edition at $3.95.

Are there paper-bound books you want
but cannot find at your retail stores? You can get any
title in print in these famous series, **POCKET BOOKS,
CARDINAL EDITIONS, POCKET LIBRARY** and
PERMABOOKS, by ordering from Mail Service Department, Pocket Books, Inc., 630 Fifth Ave., New York 20, N.Y.
Enclose retail price plus 5c per book for mailing costs.

FREE CATALOGUE SENT ON REQUEST

A
WOMAN DOCTOR
LOOKS AT
LOVE AND LIFE

by Dr. Marion Hilliard

PERMABOOKS · NEW YORK

This Permabook includes every word contained in the original, higher-priced edition. It is printed from brand-new plates made from completely reset, clear, easy-to-read type.

A Woman Doctor Looks at Love and Life

Doubleday edition published June, 1957

PERMABOOK edition published March, 1960

1st printing.......................January, 1960

A Woman Doctor Looks at Love and Life has also been published in Danish, Dutch, English, French, Norwegian and Swedish editions.

L

Copyright, ©, 1956, 1957, by Marion Hilliard. All rights reserved. This PERMA-
BOOK *edition is published by arrangement with Doubleday & Company, Inc.*
Printed in the U.S.A.

PERMABOOK editions are distributed in the U.S. by Affiliated
Publishers, Inc., 630 Fifth Avenue, New York 20, N.Y.

PERMABOOK editions are published in the United States by
Pocket Books, Inc., and in Canada by Pocket Books of Canada,
Ltd.—the world's largest publishers of low-priced adult books.

To all those women whose trust
and affection made this book possible

Contents

Introduction

A FEW YEARS AGO, when my practice in obstetrics and gynecology was at its busiest, the husband of a patient of mine approached me. "Doctor," he said, shifting rapidly on his feet, "my wife is different after a trip to your office, she's more confident and, well, better. She says you talk to her. I've been wondering, what do you tell her?"

"I don't know," I answered cautiously. "Odds and ends. About anything that seems to be bothering her. There isn't much value medically in sending her home with her worries intact."

The husband brooded over this a moment. "You mean you give your patients some kind of advice?"

"Not really. We discuss the problem together until she understands. You'd be astonished at what she understands." I grinned.

"Wonderful," he cried. "I'm managing editor of a woman's magazine, *Chatelaine*. How about writing some of that experience down in an article for us?"

"Impossible," I told him. "I haven't the time."

It was the truth. I was Chief of Obstetrics and Gynecology at Women's College Hospital in Toronto, where I operated every morning, saw a stream of patients in my office until long after darkness had fallen on the city outside, and delivered as many as forty babies every month, most of them, it seemed, at five o'clock in the morning. My life was a cycle I preferred not to think of as a squirrel cage: hospital, office, hospital, home, hospital—with side trips for speeches. I've been making speeches since I graduated from medical school twenty-five years ago, and some of them, like my annual address on marriage to a mixed audience of university graduates-to-be, have become institutions, but I believe the medical profession has a responsibility to the community. I certainly had no time for writing.

I reflected after the editor had left that I was in a remarkably tenable position to give advice to women. I had been watching the many lives of women for a quarter century: the adolescent with her terrible fears, the young wife with her dismay at love-making, the unmarried mother with terror in her eyes, the career woman, bitter because success seems empty without a man, the middle-aged woman with her longings, the older woman with her loneliness. I know them all and I would be insensitive, and a poor doctor, if I didn't try to help.

Over the years I have developed a very practical philosophy. It isn't based on idealism, because I know that hope, being false, collapses on itself, and a loss of hope can destroy the human spirit. I don't advocate contentment, which seems to me both static and smug, and I don't suggest that humans should strive for something labeled happiness, a gift that can only be transient. I must admit that I haven't much patience with modern moralizing either, although I am a religious woman.

I do believe in inevitability, the inevitability of living that produces pain and joy in unequal and unfair amounts. There is the inevitability in being human, which is the need for security, affection, status, and achievement. There is inevitability in being female, the turmoil of endocrinal change that ushers in the child-bearing years and ushers them out again thirty years later. There is inevitability in marriage, boredom, for instance, and the occasional sense of desolation. Being

2

unmarried also has its inevitable factors, notably the shredding sense of failure. All of these are inescapable as sunset, but their power to wither can be battled with wit, energy, and laughter. This is what I tell my patients: Don't waste your strength in being outraged because life is difficult for you. Assume that life naturally is difficult, will never be easier. Accept the inevitables and live vigorously.

Having said these true words, I sound like a believer in natural law only, a humanist or a stoic. True, we accept the law of the inevitable in nature first and then have faith in the power of love to change and illuminate the whole of life. There are two principles on which I stake my life. "He who will try to save his life will lose it"; and "All things are possible to them that truly love." Within this exciting paradox of belief I walk happily. Faith in the love of God is like "breathing in and breathing out."

The magazine editor continued to coax me about writing an article for him. I was tempted one night, when I was terribly weary, to have something printed somewhere warning women against fatigue. Fatigue is the most common affliction known to women, and the saddest. It robs them of vitality, without which living is a disheartening business. I was worried about the tendency of modern women to fling their energy wholeheartedly into the bonfire of ambition, and their ignorance of the danger inherent in being drained of zest day after dreary day. But nevertheless, despite my feeling that a magazine article might be of enormous benefit, I still had no time for such a project.

Then two circumstances converged to change my mind. My hospital needed a new wing and I was appointed the staff representative on a building committee. Suddenly I was fund-raising conscious. It appeared to my aroused sense of the mercenary that writing a magazine article would be an excellent way of earning

3

money for the hospital and possibly of attracting further donations. Simultaneously the magazine editor solved my dilemma about my crowded schedule. "Dictate," he said. "Just say it." The magazine would assign me a writer to help. "Would June Callwood do?" he asked.

I was delighted. Dictating was part of my daily work and comes as easily as speaking does. Also I had met June when she was a teen-ager working on a morning newspaper and interviewing me on some subject that we have both since forgotten. After that she came to me as a patient when she married another writer, Trent Frayne. I had just cared for her through her third pregnancy. I knew she was still an active writer, because only that week she had telephoned me for my opinion. I was certain it would be a fine collaboration and it has been.

"I'm going to write first about fatigue," I said.

She peered at the circles under my eyes. "Naturally," she said with a sympathetic grin.

The first article was sold off the stands a short time after it appeared and reprinted in seven countries. The next one, on a pet subject of mine, menopause, had the same acceptance. I found myself in the midst of a series that has now, as you can see, become a book.

Shortly after an article on sex and marriage had been published I received an indignant visitor.

"Just what makes you think you're an expert on marriage?" she snapped at me. "You're single!"

I kept a straight face. "It gives me an objective point of view," I pointed out to her. "A married woman only knows one man."

I know a lot about marriage, though I've never experienced it, because I have listened to the problems of literally thousands of married women. I also know, even better, the problems of unmarried women. I learned that the bitterest renunciation of all is not a mate—it is motherhood. Looking back on my life, I can chart those moments that were pivotal. The most crucial was the date I had one evening with a man I loved. He was an engineer and had been away on a project for several months. I was interning and missed him dreadfully. There was a tacit understanding that we were engaged. Together we would plan our future and set a date.

He called for me, looking brown and handsome. He had even borrowed a car. We went to dinner—I adored it—dinner away from the hospital was always a thrill. Replete, cosy in the car, waiting for my moment, while he talked of love I fell asleep. I had been on duty in the delivery room for four successive nights preceding this. He drove me home, wakened me, and said a curt good night. How thankful I've always been for that cat nap. A short time later he married someone else. He then provided me with my Gethsemane: He asked me to be his wife's doctor and deliver their first baby. It was a valuable experience. Nothing else in my lifetime has ever or will ever hurt so much. On Mother's Day, in the early morning, that I might miss no overtone of human longing or resignation, the child was born. If I could accept that and survive, and I could, then I could withstand anything.

I have said often that I have never failed to be stirred by the birth of a baby. Even at the instant that I delivered the child that might have been mine, I was moved through my anguish to feel, "This is worth while. What you are doing now is the most worth-while occupation on earth."

It is. Let me tell you about it and of what I know about women.

CHAPTER ONE

A Woman's First Baby

A HUNDRED times I have wakened in the still of a sound-less night, wide awake and suddenly excited—and listen-ing. A moment later the phone rings. It is the hospital calling to tell me that one of my patients is ready to have her baby.

I've been an obstetrician and gynecologist for twenty-five years, but a birth still seems to me the greatest treasure a life can know. The delivery room, coldly tiled and filled with stainless steel, is the pulse beat of all existence. There new lives begin, tiny humans who have never happened before. To be part of this is the most rewarding and completely worth-while part of my life.

The scene in a delivery room is especially moving when a baby is being born in the middle of the night. Outside in the darkness people are sleeping but the de-livery room is brilliant under the arc lights and filled with the concentration of a well-trained team focused on a single moment, the instant of birth. It holds a heightened sense of friendliness and tenderness rarely found elsewhere.

I want to address myself to women who are having their first baby. I think the qualities that enhance the act of giving life, the glory and greatness and pride of it, are especially glittering when a woman is carrying her first baby. The first has special fears of its own and special hazards, but it has special wonder too and a poignancy beyond all human experience.

I'm not a sentimentalist—women who refer to their infants as "bundles of love" appall me, frankly—but I'm grateful for the good judgment I had as a medical student to have chosen obstetrics. Obstetricians have the opportunity, rare in medicine, of treating the whole life of a patient rather than just the health. A surgeon participates in a single dramatic moment but an obstetrician knows the patient for twelve months during and after a pregnancy.

During these months of wonder and turmoil, there are several moments of what might be called total communication. The woman is absorbed in an honest inventory of her physical and spiritual resources and she often finds that she needs help. She is afraid, perhaps, that she lacks courage or the ability to love. She may be disappointed in herself because she is unmoved by marital love-making. She may have lost confidence in living. The heights of happiness to which an expectant mother may rise are well publicized; obstetricians alone know the depths.

Throughout the time that the doctor and patient are wrapped together in the miracle of a developing life, a spirit of trust and affection is possible. The doctor is able, operating on the sound base of this faith, to teach with lasting effect the rudiments of healthy living and to give counsel. It is an unusual woman who has sufficient inner co-ordination to adjust herself perfectly to her environment. A respected outsider like her obstetrician can sometimes brighten a black despondency with a single sentence. This is the most satisfying aspect of the practice of medicine.

One of the most valuable of the warnings that an obstetrician can give a mother waiting for her first child is that most babies are not a bit beautiful at birth. I sometimes suspect, looking at them, that the theory of original sin is true. I glance from the saintly strained face of the mother, beautiful with achievement, to the

7

unlikely scrap of person she has produced. "Your baby," I tell her, "is adorable. He looks just like your husband."

"But you've never seen my husband," the mother protests.

"Nevertheless, I'm sure of it," I assure her firmly.

Occasionally we deliver a baby who, because of dehydration, has the wizened and wise face of a prophet. He opens fathomless eyes and looks at me accusingly. "Don't look at me like that," I protest. "I had nothing to do with you being here."

Sometimes we deliver a baby who is truly beautiful, which seems to us like compounding a miracle. Sometimes we deliver a baby with a handicap. In many of these cases, no decision is required from the doctor— the baby is either healthy and strong and will survive without special attention, or else is frail and dies immediately. Others are borderline cases, infants in whom life can be supported if the staff works feverishly. My wisdom isn't sufficient to make a judgment that will let a flickering life die; we work to save the infant.

The good obstetrician a few years ago was the doctor who put his patient under heavy sedation the moment she arrived in the hospital and kept her totally unconscious throughout the entire process. The mothers wakened the next morning with no recollection at all of participating in a birth. The pendulum has swung the other way now and many mothers are enthusiastic about "natural" childbirth, without any sedation at all. I heartily approve of a woman being conscious throughout the birth because it is the highest fulfillment she will ever know and she shouldn't miss it. But how natural should childbirth be? This is the decision only an obstetrician can make, not an overeager patient and her friends. The criterion of good obstetrical care, in my opinion, is a live mother who is not

8

damaged in any way that will require a future operation or cause a chronic complaint.

In order to insure that there will not be any such residual liability, the doctor must be free to give whatever treatment might be necessary—which very commonly means instruments and stitches. I prefer for my patients a local anesthetic, which leaves them brightly awake but doesn't inhibit my decisions. However, every case is different. Just remember that no amount of good prenatal care, relaxing exercises, or freedom from fear will ever replace a well-trained doctor at any time of delivery.

The first baby is generally a shredding disillusionment. The mother has expected to feel lighter than air, to hold her infant in the mood of mutual adoration best illustrated in religious paintings, and to be worshiped by her husband. Instead she is tired to her marrow; she has afterpains, agony from her stitches, and aching bones. Her husband is nowhere to be found when she returns to her room—he's generally down the hall phoning everyone he knows. The baby isn't the sex she expected and is definitely unattractive no matter how hard she tries to convince herself otherwise. The final insult comes later when she finds that her baby has no loving instinct for nursing at all and has to be taught the basic element of survival. The wonderful, sweeping delight she has been expecting for nine months falls far short of the glory of God.

It usually takes forty-eight hours to be truly lit up about a baby, though some women have postnatal attacks of the blues three or four days later. By that time the aftermath of pain is over, the baby is nursing in his own groggy fashion, flowers have been pouring into the room, the husband's pride and concern have healed all wounds, and the mother has observed that her figure is close to normal.

Mothers of first babies are apt to feel that the infants

are fragile as blown glass. Actually the baby is in better shape than the mother. "You should see what I did to him in the delivery room," I remark, remembering the manipulations that accompanied the birth. The mother looks doubtful and I know her pediatrician is in for a busy time. If she can't hear her baby breathe she knows he's dead and if he breathes noisily she's sure he has pneumonia. One of my first night calls, at three in the morning, was to treat a baby who turned out to be suffering from hiccups.

Women who are having their first babies can expect a number of surprises, not the least of which is the personality change that accompanies pregnancy. The best illustration of this that I know is a minister's wife who was a patient of mine for her first pregnancy. One afternoon she came to me in a state of high alarm.

"Doctor," she whispered, "I'm worried about my baby."

"Your baby!" I exclaimed. "The heartbeat is just fine, the baby is developing beautifully. What on earth can be troubling you?"

"Well," she continued, in a voice approaching the inaudible. "For the first time in our marriage, I find myself extremely—ah—desirous. I'm afraid the baby will be lewd."

I still chuckle at this absurdly enchanting story. I assured the woman that her baby would not be lewd because of her behavior and explained that she was involved in the phenomenon of personality change during pregnancy. It was my unhappy responsibility to warn her that her warmth toward love-making would be as transient as her pregnancy, to the day.

I'm astonished how few people know about this dramatic change, which is as normal a part of childbearing as the change of figure. Their lack of preparation for it can have tragic results. I remember the stern young husband who came to me filled with outrage at his wife's despondency. "When we first married I thought we were in perfect agreement that we would have a big family," he told me, beginning to seethe again. "Now she's pregnant and she does nothing but mope around the house and weep. She doesn't want a baby at all, but she still keeps insisting that she does. I don't know what to make of her."

I did, and I tried to describe it. Pregnancy is accompanied by hormone change, emotional excitement, and a twinge of panic, a churning turmoil that is exhausting. During the early months of pregnancy many normally ebullient women are saturated with a lassitude that penetrates their very bones. They fall asleep at inelegant moments, as in the middle of a party or on top of their typewriters, and they have a marked tendency to mope. This attitude is out of their control, a truth that obstetricians recognized many years ago without understanding its cause.

Many times early in my practice I cared for women who seemed to me to have been consummate liars. They would describe with tender faces how they longed for children and how their arms ached to hold a baby. Later, when their pregnancies began, they would be wretched in spirit and consequently ill in body. I used to believe that these were the symptoms of a submerged resentment, just as the severe young husband had suspected, but they are not. Such women are no more masters of their queasy stomachs and gloom than they are of their girth. Their misery is increased by the strangeness of the new personality that has taken over. "I used to be cheerful in the morning," one young mother-to-be told me, watching the ceiling fixedly so she wouldn't cry. "Now I wake up wishing I was dead. I really want this baby, so why do I feel so blue?"

Just to complicate the puzzle of pregnancy's freak

despair, many women who are normally limp and passive will become for the duration of their childbearing zestful and passionate. They are glowing, feel no fatigue, and are likely to smile brilliantly at strangers. One middle-aged patient confessed to me, with impish glee, that when no one was watching she found herself skipping—bulk and all. This same warmth is spilled over in love-making, to the delight and astonishment of the husbands.

Women who get this happy reaction from pregnancy are often accredited with marvelous virtues that are only temporarily in their possession. "She must be a natural-born mother," the neighborhood agrees. "She's radiant with kindness and affection." She's radiant all right, but with the intoxicating effect she is getting from glandular change.

There is no permanent reality in either the pregnant woman who bounces with joy or the one who droops. It is part of the nature of childbearing and no one can predict which mood will devour a woman for her nine months as a perambulating incubator. This is the main reason I urge my newlywed patients to delay their first baby for a year or two until their marriage has developed sturdiness. Adjustment to connubial living is difficult enough without introducing the extra hazard of pregnancy's split-personality effects. Most obstetricians, strangely enough, are more worried by a patient who gets too gay a reaction from her pregnancy than by one who vomits, weeps, and staggers. With the birth of a baby the reaction sets in and the woman who has been creeping around in misery feels new energy and exhilaration. She recovers her normal spirits and happily tends her new infant.

She's no concern at all, but her sister, whose feet haven't touched ground for nine months, is in a bad way. Her almost hysterical energy has vanished, her former vivacity looks like soggy confetti on a dirty street and the project of caring for seven pounds of damp and noisy humanity looks insupportable. Her husband may be saddened to discover that her former attitude to love-making has returned in all its mildness. The first few months after the baby's birth take on some of the characteristics of a champagne hangover.

Because those patients whom I privately call my "floaters" are going to suffer a dismaying reaction, I feel it important to prepare them. "You're going to come down after this baby is born," I warn them as they bounce around the office grinning at themselves. I go on warning them, but I suspect I'm talking to myself. I don't have any better luck with the patients for whom pregnancy is one long, weary wake. "You're going to feel glorious when the birth is over," I told one such woman who was sagging greenly into my office chair. "I'll never make it," she replied coldly.

Such effects as these represent the extreme poles to which pregnancy can fling a female. Most women have a more moderate pregnancy, a little depressed possibly some days and a little elated on others, but usually unaffected by the growth within blooming gently and happily.

The most distressing force in pregnancy is fear. While the mother-to-be chats gaily with her relatives, shrieks with delight at baby showers, and brightly tells her doctor that everything is fine, her insides are convulsed and cold with fear. This is particularly true of the first baby. The greatest of all the fears a woman can know is the fear of the unknown. This fear is never so acute and awful as with a first pregnancy. The woman's life will be altered forever by the thing moving inside her, but how altered? What will the thing look like? How does labor feel? Will she be able to bear the pain and responsibility ahead? The woman has lost control over her future; motherhood is about to happen to her whether she is ready or not. Panic chokes her, but she feels it is unseemly and goes on pretending to be carefree.

It is the role of an obstetrician to get these fears out into the open. A buried fear can actually cause a severe inertia during labor and will certainly prolong the process unmercifully. Nothing so withers fear as examination. No one should ever be afraid alone. It is the worst form of loneliness and the most corrosive.

Most women having their first babies are working. They tell me they plan to continue working until they "show," an expression that I find exceedingly ugly. Ideally, obstetricians would have them quit work during the first three months and work during the middle three. This is obviously impractical, so we compromise by stressing the importance of extra rest. Working or not, every woman should get two hours of bonus rest daily during her pregnancy.

It is ridiculous to pretend to a woman in her first pregnancy that the months ahead will be ones of unmitigated delight. Pregnancy is uncomfortable to say the least. The stretching and moving of the muscles and joints, the vigorous activity of an infant impatient for birth and the awkwardness of the lopsided silhouette are all matters that cannot be readily dismissed. The most exasperating moments undoubtedly occur at bedtime, when the woman is trying to rest her complaining frame. She can't lie on her stomach, which may have been her favorite position, and she can't get her breath when lying on her back. She settles for her side, but when she wants to roll over she may need help. To make matters worse, she's almost certain to have to get up to go to the bathroom just as soon as she finally gets settled.

Husbands have a habit of assuming that because childbearing is a natural function for women, some internal arrangement absorbs all the discomfort. Many of them thinly veil their suspicions that their wives

14

are complaining about trivia. I'm not fond of constantly wailing women myself but I hasten to suggest that men could get some idea of the burden of pregnancy if they would consider carrying a twenty-pound golf bag around with them day and night without being able to shift it or set it aside for an instant.

It is vital that the two months before the baby is expected be dedicated to rest, because the convulsive effort of childbirth is going to require a vast reservoir of strength and endurance. Those weeks before the trip to the hospital are no time for the exhaustive house cleaning and marathon sewing dear to some home-loving but shortsighted souls.

I do advocate, for the woman who has been working, that the final months of her pregnancy be spent in learning a new trade: housework. An efficient system for doing laundry, maintaining tidiness, and preparing a meal is vital. The alternative, after the baby arrives, is pure chaos. Last week's ironing will gather mold while the carrots boil dry and empty baby bottles disturb the dust on the coffee table. The distraught woman at the core of such a situation unfortunately blames that baby and resents every demand he makes on her. It isn't the baby's fault, of course, but he's too small and unhappy to point this out.

Some of the most bedraggled humans I know are the women who are caring for infants for the first time. Their sleep is interrupted every night and they rarely miss a sunrise. They try to keep two sets of hours—an adult schedule of all-day wakefulness and late-night television viewing and an infant's whimsical notion of stirring together waking and sleeping in a twenty-four-hour caldron.

Uninterrupted sleep is impossible and the only solution this side of a breakdown is to join the baby's routine. He's thriving on his system of connected cat naps and so will his mother, once she gets the hang of it.

Some women suffer a real trauma during their first six weeks with a new baby. I've heard many say, "I've never been the same since my baby was born," and the implication is that the baby is to blame. He isn't at fault at all—the mother is suffering from defeat. She failed to cope with her child and she is ridden by frustration, fatigue, and a sense of incompetence. Looking back, she can only see that the turning point came with the birth of the baby.

Here is a tragedy that can blight the lives of both mother and child. The first necessity of motherhood is acceptance of its vicissitudes: erratic unreasonable hours, exhaustion, anxiety, and loneliness. These drawbacks are natural companions to motherhood, but impermanent.

The next necessity for every new mother is a baby sitter. Even while she is nursing her baby it's vital that she be able to slip away from her home for an hour or two with her husband. The couple needs to re-establish communication beyond the pull of the demanding little person in the crib. When the nursing period is finished, around the fourth month, the husband and wife should try to go away together for two or three days.

This is the most important point I have to make about babies; they are mere incidents in a marriage. Marriage is a relationship between man and woman that may last for fifty or sixty years. Children will come and go but the main plank remains the same. Women must always care for the needs of their husband ahead of their children. In such a home, the children and marriage will blossom. If a woman puts her children first, the children become demanding, the husband disinterested, and the wife frenzied. The health of the home will perish.

A major difficulty in the months that follow the birth of a baby is that the mother experiences a temporary

16

lull in her sexual desire. She is tired and distracted and her body is preoccupied with a major metabolic change. This same freakish frigidity occurs during menopause and I suspect it constitutes a major threat to a marriage.

I'm distressed when these new mothers lightly explain, "My husband is so understanding these days. He doesn't make any, you know, demands on me." It isn't that I'm a cynic—I'm a doctor and I know that this is an unnatural state of affairs. I'm concerned that the husband's need, which is only submerged and not vanished at all, will demonstrate itself at some inopportune time, when his wife may not be present but someone else is. Nature has no high-minded code.

I am also troubled that these so-called "good" husbands, who, prompted by sincere consideration, are making no overtures to their wives, will come to resent either the wives or their babies as the weeks of abstinence roll by.

Wives must be more sensitive to the needs of husbands, which don't vary with paternity. The women must also be sensitive to their own need to be loved and fulfilled. The period after a baby is born is one in which the new mother must be watchful that the true value of her life, which is her marriage, isn't disturbed. If she isn't careful and, if need be, a good actress, she may lose it all.

When the mother takes up the threads of ordinary living after the nursing period, she has new richness and maturity to last all her days. Her sense of importance and achievement gives her a new confidence. But all these hard-won trophies will be tarnished if the mother clings to the cocoon she has been sharing with her baby. Some women clutch at this happy time to complete dependency and domination and try to perpetuate it. Such covetous and unwholesome grasping cripples the child emotionally. The only way to keep the love and warmth of a child is to stand him on his own feet when he is ready and let him go. I want to add that this releasing of a child is just as vital in the case of adopting mothers. Women who adopt babies have special gifts from life—the joy of the phone call that notifies them that their child is waiting for them, and the giddy and unself-conscious way they can stand off and admire the baby as though he were an *objet d'art*. The special hazard in adopting is that the child is sometimes regarded as too precious to set free. It's a criminal act for an adult to cling to a child—any adult, any child.

Not long ago I delivered the baby of a favorite patient of mine who had been told when she was only a girl that she could never have a child. She nevertheless wanted a baby desperately. Her pregnancy was dreadfully difficult and dangerous; she was ill most of the time. When her baby girl was born the expression of blinding glory on the mother's face caused a moment of cathedral-like hush in the delivery room. Two months later the baby died.

When I saw the mother again I kept my tone gentle, but I have certain convictions about such things. "You wouldn't have missed that experience for anything, would you?" I asked.

She shook her head. "Doctor, I'm only sorry for you. You worked so hard and now you have nothing. I had my baby, but you have nothing."

"Don't worry about me," I replied. "I have the memory of your face in the delivery room."

The act of childbirth can light up a woman's life and it is immaterial to that experience whether or not the mother has her baby afterward. This is what I try to tell my unmarried mothers who must give up their infants for adoption and it is a truth that holds even when a first baby doesn't survive. The drama of birth, the torment wrapped with exultation beyond self, is the truest and finest moment a woman can know. It is the trial by fire that gives a soldier inner dignity to sustain him all his life. It grants a woman a piercing, dazzling pride in herself that may become dim but never dingy.

The reason for the smile on the Mona Lisa has always been clear to me.

CHAPTER TWO

What Should I Tell My Children?

~~~~~~

IT MAY seem incongruous for an obstetrician and gynecologist to be preoccupied with the raising of children, but it is a matter of pure logic—cause-and-effect variety.

I have discovered during the years that I have been treating women's ailments, the real and the imagined ones, that childhood has mighty power to maim an adult.

Sometimes it is a comparatively minor crippling, such as the girl who has witnessed her mother's groanings during menstruation and accordingly suffers from painful menstruation herself.

But sometimes the damage bites deeper and withers the womanliness of the future woman. The child may get the impression that sex is a furtive and dirty preoccupation—and the seed of frigidity is sown. If she hears her mother pity a pregnant woman, motherhood may seem shoddy to her. If she never receives the blessing of warm affection, she may never be able to give it.

A doctor can make a shrewd analysis of a patient's childhood sometimes on the basis of her attitude to illness. Some little girls are never taught to absorb small discomforts, such as growing pains and bruises, and they grow up to be women who are outraged at the aches and pains of pregnancy and hysterical during labor. Others have had an opposite training and are conditioned to be stoical. I have seen a woman with such a background close to death and still sturdily and angrily protesting that she was feeling fine.

I'm not so much interested in what mothers tell their daughters about living as in the emotional attitude that is instilled. A proper, soundly constructed attitude can see a girl through her whole life, relatively unharmed no matter what catastrophes occur. It's an annuity against abandonment to despair, fear, or grief. Teach a little girl acceptance, above all. Steady her with love and fill her with laughter.

None of this can be taught at some appointed moment convenient for the mother. It's hopeless to draw a child aside on a quiet afternoon when the ironing is done and expect that this is the time to launch a discussion about sex. The child simply won't listen. A young person hears only what she wants to hear and only when she is ready. A skillful sensitive mother may be lucky and have her chance on such an afternoon. Usually the very finest moment in the child's life to tell her about the pull of desire, for example, occurs when guests are expected at any moment. The little girl, watching her mother hurriedly fastening her earrings, suddenly asks, "How did Annie get a baby—she's not married!" The child is ready for an explanation and will listen to every word. It doesn't take long and the guests are not nearly so important.

Even if the mother is wise enough to seize the opportunity, she must also realize that anything, *anything* delivered like a sermon is unpleasant listening for a child and will be turned out. The right attitude for imparting knowledge is warmth and gentleness. I favor myself the old-style way of taking a child into your arms at such times. The closeness of mother and daughter is as essential as anything the mother is saying.

Be natural and simple in explaining reproduction to a child. It can be easily told, even in a city, with the example of familiar animals. One mother explained human procreation by using the family pet, an exceedingly amoral female cat, as an example.

"Is that how Fluffy gets her babies?" asked the child at the conclusion.

"Yes, dear," replied the mother.

"And that's how you got me?" exclaimed the child in rising surprise.

The mother nodded warily.

Suddenly the child laughed. "I think that's corny," she chuckled.

Another child, a boy of my acquaintance, was equally amused but he reacted differently. "That's the silliest thing I've ever heard," he told his mother firmly. "I don't believe a word of it."

An example of the kind of ease that I feel essential to the proper adjustment of a child was furnished by a patient of mine with a five-year-old girl. The child came home one day with a nasty case of poison ivy all over her behind. Her mother asked how the child happened to be exposed.

"Oh, we have a club," explained the little girl airily. "We call it the 'Taking Off Your Clothes Club.'"

"What do you do?" asked the mother casually.

"We couldn't decide," answered her daughter. "Some of the boys wanted to do some things but I told them I didn't think you'd go along with that. So we just take off our clothes."

A while later, when the rash had healed, the mother asked what the club planned to do.

"We're going to find a new place," her daughter assured her.

The mother looked disinterested. "Why don't you

just stop?" she suggested. "You weren't having much fun, were you?"

"No, we weren't," decided the child after some thought. "We'll stop the club."

I like this story because it illustrates how tact and a light approach can win the day, where the sledge hammer of indignation might have inflicted permanent scars and attached unwholesome suggestion to the normal curiosity of children.

Most women seem to feel that sex education begins when the tiny tot asks, "Where do babies come from, Mommy?" and the mother answers, with considerable pride in herself, "From Mommy's tummy, dear." This isn't the beginning at all; the child's sex education began when she was six months old, at the moment she started to explore her own body.

During this first and natural exploration, babies invariably discover the most erotic parts of their bodies and derive from this a pleasant sensation. Human beings are constructed in such a way that it is inevitable. The baby, being a healthy, normal little person, is making some discoveries about himself. The mother, however, may put a different connotation on what he is doing.

I once asked a former psychology professor of mine, how many children masturbate. "About 101 per cent," he answered readily. I surmised from this that masturbation is quite common among children.

A mother begins sex education with this very ordinary problem. Is she aghast? Does she slap the astonished baby's hand? Does she cry? I know for a fact that many of them phone their obstetricians, wailing so that they can scarcely be understood. Pediatricians tell me that some mothers get their husbands home from the office and insist that they deal with the potential sex fiend. None of these reactions can fail to injure the child. The notion is planted that certain areas of the body are shameful, disgusting even. The baby is being wronged, and cruelly so.

Many psychologists believe that adult preoccupation with pornography and burlesque often stems from a childhood in which natural curiosity about human anatomy was frustrated.

The solution to the universal problem of children masturbating is a positive approach, rather than the definitely harmful negative one. Recognize that in an infant such behavior is mere exploration. Give him something else to do, a toy to occupy his attention. Older children masturbate, usually, because they are bored and feel forlorn. They should be distracted with busyness. I sometimes suspect that most of the chronic behavior problems of small children can be solved by keeping them occupied. Little children have no reflections to combat idleness; they need activity. This activity often is quiet. Their pretend world holds no mischief and should be understood and respected.

Never discipline a child for masturbation and never brand it as wrong. We have to differentiate between the harmless curious exploration of a child and the guilt-ridden habit of an adolescent or adult. Unhappily, we call them both by the same name. The child's preoccupation with his body is universal and transient and is no cause for concern. The compulsive behavior of the adolescent is so riddled by fear and surrounded by an aura of disgrace that the whole personality is warped. This is a problem for the doctor or a mental-health clinic. It is not within the competence of the parents or the minister. I firmly believe that frigidity in women is often the result of the tone of voice or the atmosphere some mother has created around a child's natural interest in genitals. I wouldn't be writing about a subject so many people find distasteful if I didn't feel so strongly that it is time this shadowy menace was brought out into the light, discussed and dismissed for what it is—a normal and transient preoccupation in children.

An easy nudity in the home around bathing and swimming activities is the best and most natural method of settling curiosity, but I do wish the contemporary trend in this direction was more restrained. Many young couples, in their anxiety to keep any hint of furtiveness away from sex, fail to draw any boundaries of good taste. I've seen a child of eight, stark naked, stroll unconcernedly through the living room while guests were present. A rather charming dinner party was disrupted only recently when a ten-year-old blithely referred to procreation on the canine level. It is surely not overwhelmingly difficult to advise children on the unsuitability of certain topics and certain behavior outside the family circle.

Similarly, some mothers are so determined to be frank (their word) about sex education that they dazzle the child with pyrotechnics of detailed explanation, both bewildering and boring. Make certain first what information the child wants and give it to him, with no added flourishes. I might add the caution that some children aren't interested at all in reality and will discard science every time.

The mother of one such child was stunned to hear her little daughter informing a cohort that the fairies leave babies under rosebushes.

"I told you how babies are born, didn't I?" the mother asked, drawing the child aside.

"Oh sure," answered the little girl, "but I like this better."

Every mother must attempt to judge, although impartiality is impossible, what sort of child she has. Some children want a leavening of fantasy in their lives and won't thrive without it. Mothers in such cases must make a distinction between reality and frills—but recognize that each has value. Other children want the facts, like cops, just the plain facts.

All of them need to know that the theme of reproduction is respect, kindness, responsibility, and affection. They learn this through their pores, absorbing the atmosphere of the home. The relationship between the parents establishes the tone that the children will always associate with marriage.

For this reason I feel it is one of the greatest of modern tragedies that fathers have so little time for their children. One survey in the United States established that the average father spent seven minutes a week in direct, personal communion with his children. Children in such homes naturally grow up believing that their mother is the kingpin of the universe, an attitude that may enchant the mother but can only cause difficulties for the children.

A little girl who is raised by an absentee father and an enthusiastic mother can never have a properly focused understanding of marriage. In searching for a mate, she has no pattern to make a sensible judgment. A little boy has just as great a problem. He cannot see the stature of being male; he has no concept of the protectiveness and strength of his sex. When he marries he is without any workable appreciation of the role of a husband.

Parents should never be rude to one another—at least not in front of the children. The father shouldn't be irritable or the mother full of tears. A child can accept occasional disagreements between the adults he loves, but not the acid evil of constant dislike and insult. A father can teach his son a good attitude towards sex in the courtliness and consideration he shows his wife. A mother can teach the grass-roots principle of happy adjustment in the respect and admiration she shows her husband. This is sex education in its finest, most intelligent form.

Even in the all-too-common households where pressure of business keeps the father absent a good deal of the time, the mother can do much to rescue the situation. She must keep clearly in mind, for the sake of the family as a whole, that the father is its head. She must never deride his wisdom or his decisions. She must never give the child the impression that only she, his mother, is interested in his activities. The multitude of monologues that distinguish a child's conversation should be directed at the father as well—and he would be well advised to listen patiently and with interest if he hopes to retain the friendship of his offspring. A breach between father and children is painfully difficult to bridge.

In the field of obstetrics, with its acute emotional impact, the quality of the childhood training can be clearly discerned in the adult patient. Some women approach motherhood with such obvious delight that they all but giggle. I know full well that their mothers loved babies and were proud in pregnancy. Some women are nervous and look at me with fathomless panic when I confirm their suspicion that they are pregnant. I can make an astute guess about their mothers too.

I wish mothers would remember that everything they say to their daughters about babies forms an attitude that persists a lifetime. One of my patients years ago told me, "The happiest time in our family is when I'm pregnant." When she was having her fourth child the older children were concerned that their two-year-old brother was too small "to remember how wonderful it is to have a baby." They used to put his tiny hands on his mother's tummy so that he could feel the life within. "Mummy, baby," he would say, under their coaching. Not long ago the oldest child of the household, now grown and married, came to me to have her first baby. She was absolutely radiant and, possibly only by coincidence, she had one of the easiest pregnancies and deliveries in my experience.

My own choice of obstetrics as a profession is rooted, I am certain, in an incident that happened when I was five years old. My mother took me into our guest room —I remember it was chilly because it was unheated unless we had company—and pulled open the bottom bureau drawer. The smell of camphor and cashmere stung my nostrils and I saw the drawer was filled with beautiful baby clothes.

"This is our secret," my mother told me, with a sweetness in her face. "We are going to have a baby."

"Does Daddy know?" I whispered.

My mother chuckled and closed the drawer. "You can come here whenever you like and look at the baby's things," she told me.

I learned of the tenderness and responsibility of having a baby in those few moments. For many years the thought of babies evoked the smell of camphor and cashmere and the loving tone of my mother's voice. I wish all women could have such an introduction to childbearing. It would settle something that too often is in doubt—that the business of creation is happy and fundamental. Babies are the result of warm love that overflows into physical union. That's my idea of sex education.

I don't want to leave this subject of sex education and the child without dealing with a problem that few people realize is very common. In a staggering number of homes, young children are having unpleasant sexual experiences with older people. It happens sometimes when a maid cares for a young boy or with an older male relative and a little girl. The experience is usually trivial in nature but nevertheless destructive in its consequence. I am certain that much of the exaggerated revulsion of some brides is the result of a traumatic experience in their childhood. I'm caring for two such girls now; their menstruation is erratic and their loathing for the physical side of love is deep-rooted.

Almost all parents warn their children to be wary of a "stranger." It is a fact, familiar to experts studying sexual deviation, that most incidents of this nature occur with an adult whom the child knows and trusts, a relative or a neighbor. Children should be cautioned to avoid all interference from any source. It isn't necessary to be specific and describe the detail of deviation, of course, but make it clear that the child mustn't permit interference *from anyone*.

Should some such episode befall your child despite all the protective devices you have built, I urge you to submerge your anguish and try to forget it. Treat the child with the same warmth and relaxed affection as in the past. In my experience, the hand-wringing overwrought mother is a far greater hazard to the child's recovery than the experience itself.

"What should I tell my children about—you know," a neurotic patient of mine once asked me, squirming in her chair and twisting her gloves. "They ask me questions and I just don't know what to say."

I looked at her beaten, harrowed face and listened to the whine in her tone and I didn't know how to advise her. There is very little such a woman can tell children that will be of benefit, because the atmosphere she creates is all wrong.

But the mother who meets life with gaiety, who fills her home with companionship and consideration and a brimming zest, such a mother can tell her children that babies come from the moon, by parachute, if she likes. She won't, but it probably wouldn't matter much if she did. Her children will make out all right. They're going to just love being people.

CHAPTER THREE

Adolescence

~~~~~~

I HAVE a niece who, when she was thirteen years old, was standing in front of a mirror just before she was to leave for a party. She was wearing a lovely, fluffy party dress, her white gloves were immaculate, her hair was curled and shining with cleanliness and she looked heartbreakingly sweet. She stared at her image for a moment and her face grew sad. "Mother," she sighed, "I can't act the way I look."

This remark, by a child with wisdom beyond her years, seems to me to wrap most of the problems of adolescence into a single package. An adolescent is a budding woman, but she feels desperately unready for womanhood. She may look like a girl who has everything: becoming clothes, doting parents, attractiveness, but within herself she is consumed with perpetual anxiety.

In my almost thirty years of caring for women, as their obstetrician and gynecologist, I have known hundreds of adolescents. I've heard the story from both sides, because I have known their mothers too. This time I'd like to address myself to the girls, understanding full well what a staggering responsibility I am taking on.

Adolescence is a time of decision. It is only a few years since you put away your dolls, but now you must make decisions worthy of an aged philosopher. What career will you choose? What do you think about God?

You're old enough to have learned that cheaters sometimes do prosper. How do you now feel about integrity? You've been told you live in a country that believes all men equal, but you know that a Negro can't buy a cup of coffee in some restaurants. You used to think your parents were the world's most perfect beings; lately you are discovering that they are fallible. How do you feel about them? Do you know what kind of mate you want? Do you know how to operate on a budget? Do you even know what sweater to wear to school today?

Adolescence is also a period of growth, lasting usually from the age of ten or eleven until about seventeen. But it isn't only physical growth. There is also a massive upheaval in the entire nervous system as the endocrine glands go about their functions of changing a child into a childbearing woman. Some girls go through adolescence fairly serenely and others are rocked by constant emotional storms.

I must say here that adolescence is not the only time in your life when you will be confused, unreasonable, insecure. The same process happens again when you arrive at menopause. This, in fact, is the opposite side of the same coin. You are just entering the cyclic life of fertility and the woman in menopause is just leaving it. Both are frightened of the future: you dread the responsibility of maturity and the older woman sees ahead of her uselessness and loneliness. Neither of you can stand much criticism; it is a time for tenderness, laughter, and easy forgiveness.

Regard for a moment one of the various kinds of misery of adolescence. At fourteen you may suddenly shoot up to five foot ten. You are taller than most boys your age and because of this you are in a hot agony of doubt that you will be admired by the opposite sex. In addition, you will look older than your age and you are expected to act accordingly. Adult behavior, however, is impossible for you. After all, you are only four-teen.

Whatever your physical dimensions, your ability to grapple with any of adolescence's problems will be complicated by a constant fatigue, caused by the glandular change within you coupled with a spurt of growth. This accounts for your outrageous posture, for your languid attitude toward chores, and your habit, which doesn't enthrall your parents, of lying on the floor to read or talk on the telephone. For this reason I suggest that you take a less enraged view of the house rules that compel you to be in by a certain time on school nights. They are not designed to persecute you, as you seem to suspect. An early bedtime for teen-agers is necessary to protect your health. You need extra rest when you are pregnant, when you are nursing, when you are in meno-pause—and when you're an adolescent. There's no point in bucking the system. Believe me, a doctor; it's bigger than you are.

In the midst of all the changes to your body, adolescence is going to change your personality for a few years. When you were ten you knew for sure that you were the apple of your parents' eye. Right now you are convinced that no one loves you. You seem to see life through the distortions of an amusement-park mirror. You and your parents seem to be locked in some terrible struggle to determine who will possess you, yourself or they. Your friendships, instead of being easy and happy, are pitched to a screaming point with jealousy and over-sensitivity.

Many things are happening to you these days, but most disturbing of all is the battle with your parents. You have been in the cocoon of childhood, completely protected by your parents. Now their slightest attempt to protect or advise you appears to you to be aimed at postponing the moment when your adult wings will be ready.

31

Consider with your sometimes real wisdom the position of your parents. They have been accustomed to helping you make your decisions and solve your problems. At a time in your life when they know, quite accurately, that you need them most, you are pushing them away. They are ravaged with concern for you because the choices you make now will bind you all your life, but you resent even their interest. Give a little on this. Talk to your parents and see if they won't give a little too. You must have the freedom to make your own mistakes but permit them to define for you which mistakes are harmless, if uncomfortable, and which are irrevocably blighting.

Among the latter are surely the mistakes that young girls make with sex. A terrible emotional insecurity comes from the shock of recognizing sex. Up until adolescence boys and girls have taken little note of their gender. Suddenly, in the space of what may be a moment or months, they come upon the realization that sex is an earth-shaking power. They are terrified and fascinated. They are too young to cope with it, but it fills their minds and bodies.

All teen-agers are acutely aware of the strong pulse of sex within them. I am not a person whose morals are shaped by convention, but I would sternly advise all of you to hold off much investigation of its force. You mustn't let it dominate you because this is the wrong time for it. A person's life is sorted out in airtight compartments: a time for being born, a time for dying; a time for loving and a time for learning. This is your time for learning, the only time you will get until you die. On your learning depends your knowledge and on your knowledge depends your career, your marriage, your ability to be a good mother, and the wisdom that will direct your life. These years of learning are too important to be overwhelmed by passions. Put education first just now; afterward you'll have fifty years left for loving.

Some experience with sex, by and large, is a good thing. From adolescence onward it is as much a part of life as breathing, and it must and will be examined by the young and curious. I doubt very much that any but a minute minority of young girls really want to experience sex in its fullest form. I therefore have some advice, some simple ground rules, on the subject of control. First of all, don't be so foolhardy as to trust yourself. You're not made of cast iron, you're flesh and warm blood. Protect yourself by making sure that you and your date are never in a location where outside influences cannot inhibit you. Empty houses and parked cars make ideal settings for disaster. The absence of your mother and father is not a license for necking. Never neck because you have nothing else to do or because you feel you have to pay for your date. Make certain that there is a good likelihood of interruption.

Some girls have such an overwhelming desire for marriage that schools seem to have little value beyond that of happy hunting ground. This is sheer shortsightedness. I have no complaint against early marriages as such, but I am unalterably opposed to young girls shortchanging themselves on their educations. This is one of the dangers inherent in dating steady, and the other risk is that the couple may decide to marry while the boy continues his education and the girl supports them both. She is making a tragic mistake. I know of countless broken marriages that have resulted from such an arrangement. The girl doesn't mind the hard work of her life, but the boy can't bear the load of gratitude he must carry. He finds someone else, someone with whom he can feel tall again. It's a sad story for both of them.

Unfortunately this area of adolescence and sex is the one in which parents feel the most anxiety and children the most withdrawal. You teen-agers chat glibly with your mothers about superficialities and keep nine tenths of yourselves underwater, like icebergs. When asked, "How was the party, dear?" you recite a roll call of who was there and throw in a few details about what someone wore or the food. You don't answer the questions that were really asked: "Were you comfortable? Are your manners and training adequate to get you through all situations? Did you have any trouble in the back seat after the party?" If you and your mother have never been friends, you'll never answer those unspoken questions. If you have been pals in the past, for the sake of the old relationship reassure her. She's been all-important to you for most of your life, it's hard for her to find herself so abruptly a spectator.

Adolescence is a state that must run its course. In the end you're going to have much the same values and principles that you had as a child. You'll have tested them, kicked them, and lost them entirely during the process of growing up but, if they were worthy, they'll return healthier and more durable than ever.

Another low blow that parents have to endure is that teen-agers seek guidance all right, but they never go to their parents. Getting help from mother is a mark of immaturity in an adolescent's book; getting help from an outsider has the stamp of adulthood. You get your help from a teacher, an aunt, or even a fond neighbor. (Boys go to a YMCA counselor or their football coach.) You hold long and earnest conversations, revealing a labyrinth of intrigue and examining inferences and intentions with the insight of the hypersensitive. Be careful that you are not exchanging the domination of your parents for the domination of a stranger. Some adults can't resist the temptation to play Svengali with young people.

Another learning process dear to your hearts is the ceaseless exchange of experiences and confidences with people your own age. Like a group of suburban mothers

34

pooling their information about the treatment of measles, you're charting your way through adolescence. Every day you pick up a new piece of information, a new clue to eventually solve the mystery of becoming mature.

During all this self-preoccupation, you can't bear to be different. Your mother hates this conformity but she's discovered it's a waste of money to buy you Bermuda shorts if the rest of the gang is wearing khaki jeans. Your present desire to dress like your friends won't be a life-long fixation—the thought that is alarming your mother —but right now it is a real necessity.

This urge for conformity includes your parents. You want them to be exactly like everyone else's parents, which is unfair. You cringe when your mother laughs too loudly and wince when your father cuts the front lawn in shorts. Your mother never looks right to you: either she dresses too casually or too ornately; her hair style is awful; her figure disgusts you. Kindly remember, young lady, that she looked pretty marvelous to you the time she sat up all night when you were eight and nursed you through pneumonia. Try to realize that she will look pretty wonderful again when you've had a fight with your husband and your pride needs patching. Right now you feel she's a hazard to your development. It's her presence that annoys you, not her general appearance. If she's wise, she'll wait you out patiently and put up with your criticism. Some parents fight back with humor, which is the best weapon.

"Goodness!" one girl shrieked at her mother, a patient of mine. "Your hair is full of gray!"

"Thank heavens you noticed it," replied her mother imperturbably. "I was afraid you were color-blind."

A father I know was chuckling over his own wit just the other day. His son had accused him of letting himself become flabby, unlike the man next door who exercised regularly.

"Lying in this position," the father told him loftily, "I am able to devote all my strength to keeping my brain limber so that I can deal with my upstart children."

Take it easy on your parents, girls. You're going to find them remarkably improved in a few years.

One of the major wars between adolescents and their parents, as I mentioned earlier, is rules. You argue tirelessly about bedtime, homework, allowances, household chores, and the curfew on dates. Some parents, not yours I hope, try to buy their children's favor by giving them privileges. This inculcates the young people with a fine sense of blackmail. You'll be skeptical about this, unless you're extremely honest within yourself, but you really want rules. You're kicking at the fences to make sure they're really there.

I'm reminded of something a mother overheard her daughter say in a telephone conversation, when she was explaining to another girl that she couldn't go with her to a late movie. "I just can't!" the teen-ager was saying. "My mother really cares about me. She doesn't let me come home so late."

If you'll forgive a digression, my prenatal patients often remind me of adolescents. They complain to me about the things I have advised them not to do, like paint the living room or go for a long car trip. They don't really want to paint the living room or go on a trip at all. They just want to make sure that I'm taking care of them.

I may add, for the benefit of parents who may be reading this, that I think they are making a terrible mistake if they compel their daughters to live by the same rules that applied a generation ago. Such practices as early dating are now normal. Only devastating friction can result from a parent's refusal to recognize changing standards. A teen-ager cannot exist in her group under old-style restrictions. She will become an outcast and blame her parents, rightly.

It is a time for delicate maneuvering. If the other children in the community are going to a dance although they are only thirteen, then your daughter should be permitted to go too. You discuss with her the simple good manners she will require at the dance, courtesy, consideration for the bashfulness of boys and so on, and you lead up to an agreement on the time she must come home. It is important that the girl agree on this curfew as being fair. She can't respect a curfew arrived at dictatorially.

While I'm talking to parents I'd like to add that I believe they get a second chance with their adolescent children. The first chance to do a good job and lay down the patterns of a lifetime comes in the first five years of the child's life. Some parents muff this one through inexperience or, possibly, because they are too immature themselves. But during adolescence the child is shaken out of the pattern that was developing. Here is a second opportunity to instill, without sermonizing, a sense of justice and honor.

You can't simply set aside an hour a day for Character Formation. Communication with an adolescent is a frail thing. It won't be bullied into being and it won't be coaxed. It is done subtly, by creating an atmosphere of mutual trust and confidence in the home and giving the child an opportunity to chat without interruptions or distractions. The rebuffs and withdrawals will outnumber the moments of sharing, but those fragments will be golden and worth the effort.

I have a theory about how adolescents can help themselves that I'd like to describe. I suspect the most effective method of combating the anguish of these trying years is to get away from interior thinking. It's natural to examine every pore in the mirror, to be desperately anxious to be popular, to be involved in a chain daydream of your own eventual importance, but you don't have to carry on that way all the time. Figure out for yourself the best way of getting a release from yourself. It may be sports or it may be worship, which includes for me church, music, nature, art, or other elements whose value is entirely to the spirit.

During this time of rejecting parents and the life of the family there must be something else to fill the vacuum besides yourself. It's one of the paradoxes of life that something which enlarges the spirit, which isn't tangible, invariably enlarges the personality and understanding, which are more palpable.

This sort of spiritual stretching should be an active thing, pursued vigorously. In adolescence nothing stands still. If it does, I'm alarmed. The teen-age girl who never argues with her mother and spends her time helping around the house or being alone in her room really frightens me. She's not growing up at all, she's deliberately staying a child. Maturity can never be achieved without a struggle. I'd suggest that such a girl is truly in need of professional help.

In your search for independence, you teen-agers can be very trying to elderly people over twenty, you know. Your music is full of awful rhythms to my ears. Your heroes are sometimes startling. Your preference, despite the pine-paneled recreation room at home, is for other pine-paneled pastures. Teen-agers rarely are comfortable in their own homes, and I'm aware that this is a healthy symptom of growing up.

Even your untidiness, if you've worried about this (which I doubt), is normal and natural. You've got such a roaring disturbance going on within you that you haven't time for details such as picking up your clothes or keeping your fingernails clean. But your parents will be cheered in a few years to discover that your Tobacco Road period isn't permanent.

I'd like to add a few words about graciousness. I recently visited a group of young housewives who had simplified their chores with a number of short cuts. They served soft drinks at their gatherings and drank them out of the bottle; they helped themselves to cookies still in the bakery carton. I know those women very well and I've seen them glide with the ease born of good breeding down a formal reception line. But I wonder about their children. What chance have they to learn of gentle living?

I'd recommend for every well-rounded family a formal Sunday dinner, with candles and real napkins on the table and everyone dressed in his best. Jewish families do this beautifully on Friday evenings. It's an occasion for learning attitudes of respect (how many teen-age boys have been instructed on how to hold their mother's chair?) and the benign influence of such meals offsets the bad period of adolescence when all boys behave like boors and all girls tend to chew gum. I've known families where this sort of state dinner has been a regular custom for years and it is treasured for the jewel it is. Mother puts out her best food and Father puts out his best conversation. Their children react in a way that is a good omen for the future—they bring their best friends.

The most vital piece of wisdom that I can tell you about is the inevitability of life. Each act is followed, without fail, by a consequence. True responsibility can only come from your own inner discipline. It is the most valuable lesson a human can learn. I doubt very much that it can be taught, but I'll tell you how I found out about inevitability.

In our large family we divided up the responsibility for taking care of our cow. As I remember it, my oldest brother was supposed to milk her. I was supposed to bring her in from the field every evening. I hated that job passionately because I was afraid of the dark and a little afraid of the cow. I tried getting someone to go with me, I tried to trade jobs with someone else, and I tried putting it off so that someone would go in my place. Nothing worked. No matter how I twisted and tried, I always had to get that cow.

Eventually I learned the great truth. The best way, the only way, was to get the cow right on time and get the job over with. Delaying inevitably meant that it would be even darker when I eventually had to fetch her. I've been applying that same knowledge all my life to jobs I didn't want to do; I just buckle down and get them over with. It was the most useful lesson I ever learned.

Every teen-ager must learn, in some form or other, the law of inevitability. The time has come when parents no longer discipline and decide. The decisions must be made by yourself and bolstered by the discipline that comes of appreciating consequence. You will never be an adult, no matter how long you live, until you learn it. Sometimes when I see an adolescent flailing around with some assigned task, putting it off and obviously hopeful that her parents will help her out, I have a wayward thought. It's too bad every family doesn't have a cow.

CHAPTER FOUR

Woman's Greatest Hazard

I AM often dismayed by the modern woman who appreciates so sharply that human behavior can fall into predictable patterns and then fails to apply that knowledge to herself. Most women are aware that four-year-olds are restless, adolescents are dramatic, and women in menopause are gloomy. At the same time they continue to believe, with ridiculous pride, that their problems in sex relations are rare curiosities.

Actually any doctor can chart the progress of love-making in marriage—a strained honeymoon, a span of approximately five years before sexual adjustment is perfect, a crisis after ten years because both partners are full of yearnings and misery, another crisis after twenty-five years because of an overwhelming sense of bleakness.

I've heard ten thousand tales of woe. They boil down to two or three different plots with infinite variations. Everything that can happen to a woman during love-making, comical, cruel, tragic, or beautiful, has happened before. This is important, and deeply comforting, for women to know. There is enormous therapeutic value in a wife's learning that her problem is not unique and insoluble, but universal and solved every day.

I want to deal in another chapter with the larger subject of sex throughout the lifetime of woman, particularly with sex and the unmarried woman, but first let me discuss sex in marriage. It's a relationship potentially as lovely and as lethal as a rope bridge over a chasm; it is capable of exalted beauty or sour doom. And, contrary to popular opinion, it is the woman and not the man who determines whether the act of love will enrich her life or curse it.

The male invariably arrives at marriage with the conviction that love-making is a straightforward simple pursuit with certain fulfillment. He is so constructed that, while the atmosphere of love-making may vary considerably, his own enjoyment is relatively constant. Women, on the other hand, are deeply dependent for their enjoyment on the atmosphere. It must be just so, with no distractions, no jarring moments, no annoyances, or else she is incapable of genuine response.

For this reason wise women throughout the centuries have created an aura of fragile beauty around the act of love. Tenderness, music, and perfume are part of the setting a female requires. The male can get along just as well without them, but the right mood is imperative to her.

41

When I was a younger doctor I used to believe that all my bride patients needed for a successful marriage was some education. A few facts about their physical composition, a brief and clinical description of the sex act and a few words on the male need and these brides were all set—or so I thought. I now appreciate that the happiness of women in love-making has a much more tenuous basis than any textbook can illustrate. Women are born with more sensitivity and intuition than men, for very practical reasons. These extra senses must be cultivated and nourished in order to enrich love-making; without them the act of love can be a barren experience for a woman.

I don't mean to say that a bride, to be happy, requires only a sharpened sense of the ethereal. She also requires, urgently, a visit to her doctor. A great many women could be spared pain and humiliation during their honeymoons by the simple precaution of a medical examination. Every obstetrician in the land has met women married for months or even for ten or twelve years who are still technically virgins because they failed to have a premarital checkup and later were too embarrassed to approach a doctor until the desire for children drove them to it. "My husband doesn't suffer," they explain lamely, their faces turning crimson and their eyes sliding away. Of course he doesn't—but the woman walks on white coals of shame and defeat.

Love-making, I have decided, is woman's greatest hazard. If she overcomes the difficulties, her life will be radiant; if she fails, the misery is enduring. I often think of the two women who came into my office, one after the other, on an afternoon many years ago. The first one wore pink and her face wore a dazzling luster. She had been married three months and it had been an ecstatic union. The next woman had also been married about three months but she wore gray from head to foot and her face and voice matched her clothes. "Why didn't someone tell me," she wailed, "that getting married was so horrible!"

I have used this story of the two brides with the conveniently contrasting costumes and attitudes whenever I am asked to address some group on the problems of marriage. How had the first bride achieved so much happiness and why had the second achieved so little?

To begin with, the first girl had a sense of humor. It is illogical to assume that the pursuit of love-making is a grave and stern endeavor. It can be a wildly hilarious undertaking. The first surgical patient I saw in my medical career, back when I was a student, was a woman who fell out of bed while joyfully making love and broke her arm. Her mishap seemed to her the height of comedy. It may seem a macabre form of humor but it illustrates my point that solemnity has little place in a marriage bed.

The highly unskilled honeymoon stage of love-making requires a sense of the ridiculous more than any subsequent period. It is a well-established biological fact that males in the early nervous days of a marriage are often unsatisfactory lovers. When this happens the bride has her husband's self-esteem at her mercy. With her sense of pouting injury she can at that moment build an edifice of humiliation or else she and her husband can be greatly amused—and build a marriage.

The other important difference between my two contrasting brides is that the happy one had a nature that was instinctively giving. She was the type of girl who hugged her grandmother, snuggled babies against her neck and lent her best cashmere sweater. She went into marriage with a whoop, ready to praise the smallest talent, appreciate the slightest show of thoughtfulness, and acknowledge her husband's pride in his own masculinity. Her husband rewarded her as she deserved, loving her with zest and tenderness born out of his confidence.

The second bride had a different attitude. She was uncomfortable about open affection because her composure was too thin to risk a rebuff. She was afraid of sex in the various ways that a woman can fear sex. The inconsequential fears are those of physical pain and loss of dignity. The greater fear is of vulnerability: the first act of love for many women means that they are no longer intact and in control of their person—and I am not speaking of the physical. They can only regard love-making as a surrender to a violation. There is no giving in their interpretation of love-making, but only as much a withdrawal as the nature of the act permits.

A tendency of a woman who is afraid of sex is to avoid seeking help. She has no clarity of thought; she believes in the great myth started by the brothers Grimm—that people in love marry and automatically live happily ever after. She prepares for marriage by reading romantic fiction and bolsters her hopes with the blissful lives of paper heroines. If she should bring herself haltingly to confide her uncertainties to her fiancé she will get no help at all. Men invariably believe in their own ability to master any situation that terrifies a woman, from setting mousetraps to launching a marriage. "Don't worry," he murmurs, "I'll take care of you."

He means well but he is incapable of overcoming the basic difficulty, that his bride is not prepared to give. She is hurt and outraged on her honeymoon, casting herself in the role of sacrificial virgin and him in the unbecoming raiments of an uncouth rapist. After a while she comes to her doctor and whines that marriage is a misery.

Another puzzlement is the woman who is ardent during all premarital embraces and cold during the marriage act. "But she looked so sexy!" a husband once complained to me of such a wife. The difficulty is the neurotic image that the young woman has formed as a result of too much peering at Tab Hunter. She is convinced that love is a series of caresses, requiring nothing more of her than a shiver of delight. She is unprepared for the giving needed in the act of love.

Sex attraction between man and woman is a happy thing. It's exhilarating and gay and unspeakably sweet, once it has been learned. But it is an activity which needs experience and practice, like any activity of the mind and body. Absurd and unforeseen things will happen, especially in the early years. The timing of the climaxes can take five years to perfect, during which time the wife must be prepared to comfort her chagrined husband.

"It isn't going to work the way you expect it," I warn the brides who come to me for advice. "Just relax and enjoy yourself. Don't be self-conscious."

I have abandoned completely what used to be part of my talk with brides. I had noted that a bride usually arrives at her marriage bed in a state of exhaustion bordering on hysteria. The emotional tangle of leaving her independence, the endless shopping, the series of parties, and the strain of deciding on china patterns and the color of drapes have worn her out. As a doctor, I used to prescribe rest. "You're going to live with this man for fifty years," I would say. "You can put off love-making until you get enough sleep."

One afternoon a bride who had received this advice returned to my office. Haltingly and with pink confusion, she told me that she and her husband had postponed love-making, as I had suggested.

"That's fine," I said. "I hope everything went well."

"But, Doctor!" she burst out. "We haven't started yet! We're both so embarrassed and there just doesn't seem to be the right moment." I was so shaken by this shy disaster that I never again advocated delay.

I also used to believe that if women had no fear of pregnancy they would enjoy a sex life to the same extent and in more or less the same way as men. I was wrong.

A woman's reaction to sex has few points of resemblance with a man's. For one thing, her climax varies from one so slight that it is a sigh to one so profound and deep that it results in an agonizing cry. A man's emotion varies, but his physical climaxes are identical. Millions of women feel nothing, nothing at all; others are so moved that there is a small death within them and they weep. The same woman can experience the whole galaxy of climaxes, from the top to the bottom, depending on her mood. The male enjoyment of sex requires no mood except the basic desire.

Women show their finest control of sex in their most complete surrender. A woman can stage her love-making with candles and champagne, decide on the moment to permit it to happen, set the mood—whether abandoned, frisky or gentle—and then must have the wit to dissolve. The hunter-male is delighted with his victory, but the wife scores the greater triumph. He would have enjoyed himself in any case; she desperately requires an atmosphere of loveliness or else the experience is wasted.

A man can feel kinship with the gods if his woman can make him believe he can cause a flowering within her. If she doesn't feel it, she must bend every effort to pretense. A husband may be offended by this. He does not want a service rendered. He wants love freely given. I am making a fundamental distinction between loving and making love. A wife loves, therefore she woos a tired mate when she knows he needs her. The pretense is only in her physical reaction to the act itself. There is no greater gift and it should be treasured. It's the worthiest duplicity on the face of the earth; I heartily recommend it to discontented wives. It gives a man his manhood, a quality of glorious robustness that cannot fail to reward the giver. Thousands of women who have begun this sort of benign sham have discovered that their pretended delight rapidly became real.

Many women are ravaged by concern because their

climaxes fail to cause the earth to move. My favorite, most consoling analogy is the sneeze. A sneeze is an orgasm of the nose and some sneezes are kitten-soft and others can be heard for two blocks. The kitten-soft sneeze is enjoyable and provides a lovely sense of relief; the Gargantuan sneeze is almost an agony and leaves behind it limp lassitude.

Another of the areas of difference between the sex act of men and women is distraction. Not much, short of ridicule or a gun barrel between his eyes, can distract a man during the act of love. There is very little in civilization that won't distract a woman and rob her of her joy.

For example, some women are distracted by light and can only enjoy love-making in the dark. Very few women, I have discovered, prefer love-making in the sunlight and I find this singularly hard to understand. Women also cannot respond in a room with thin walls when there are other people in the building. A child crying, a telephone ringing, and the spell is broken.

One favorite patient of mine came to me one day with the life gone from her face. She dragged herself to a chair and slouched down wearily.

"What has happened?" I asked in some concern. After a time she told me. Her father-in-law, it appeared, lived with them and it was his habit to read every night until two in the morning. She had become so inhibited that she was whipped, spiritually and emotionally.

"Besides," she added in a dull voice, "the catch on our bedroom door doesn't work properly. It keeps opening."

"On your way home," I advised her, "stop in a hardware store and buy a strong padlock and an alarm clock. Set the alarm clock for four in the morning."

She grinned and left. I knew she wouldn't buy the alarm clock, and she didn't, but she invested in the best lock she could buy. A few months later when she came to me for her first baby she was radiant.

"That big lock has made all the difference," she sighed. "I feel safe and life has been much better."

Another strongly adverse influence on women in love-making is weariness. A woman needs to concentrate so much physical energy into love-making that she cannot be tired. A woman suffering from fatigue has a tendency to put off the act of love in the expectation that she will feel more like it later. This is a fallacy. The sexual appetite needs nourishing or it withers, just as a stomach shrinks during a diet. A woman who puts off love-making is going to feel less and less inclined.

A patient of mine who was married to a minister came to me sheepishly with another problem. She and her husband enjoyed one another once a week, on Sunday nights. It left her exhausted the next morning, when she had to face an enormous weekly washing.

"I've tried to persuade him that this is very difficult for me," she complained, "but it is no use. Is there something I could do about it?"

"Certainly," I said promptly. "Wash on Tuesdays."

Some marriages have no time for love. The couple is busy with parties and small children and building a business success, and weeks go by without a union. There simply doesn't seem to be room on the agenda for it. This is a dangerous situation; love-making is a human need, a comfort for the body, a soother for nerves and a brightening influence on the spirit. Time must be reserved for love, or else the marriage is a frantically scurrying emptiness. In the midst of the hustle, the woman must cherish an oasis that is private, quiet, and serene. This is vital.

I believe that a happy bedroom is the core of a marriage. A place where the husband and wife can withdraw from the pressure of business and financial worries and fretting over the children's behavior, and find in each other a source of strength that stems from their mutual confidence. This oasis gives a man the assurance that he is vigorous and skillful and the woman the knowledge that she is needed and prized.

Many people agree that children draw their sense of security from the knowledge that they are loved and their parents love one another. The awareness of this love between the parents envelops a child and warms him. Knowing that my parents had this oasis in the midst of the hurly-burly of our large family and many guests gave me infinite delight as a child. The world was all right, I reasoned, because my parents were all right.

A husband needs his wife when he is depressed and irritable. The moments of love when a man is exultant and contented are luxuries; a man in need is a snapping turtle and a wise wife can give him back contentment very simply.

Women should also be prepared for another poorly understood facet of love-making. The height of the climax in some cases is matched by a subsequent sense of despair. There is a moment of bleakness when both parties feel deserted and this can be disturbing because it seems unreasonable. Actually it is completely normal, fitting itself comfortably in with the law of nature which dictates that for every action there is an opposite re-action. The antidote is the comfort of an embrace, rather than the turning away that usually follows.

I'd like to return to something I said in the beginning: that the patterns of sexual behavior seem to repeat themselves to the point of predictability. This cannot be demonstrated more dramatically than by looking at a marriage ten years old. Some marriages, I realize, mature more rapidly and come to the stage I am about to describe when they are only five or six years old. These are exceptions, marriages that have endured mammoth conflicts and turbulence and therefore age more rapidly.

The couple married ten years has arrived at a cross-roads. The tenth year is a blast furnace that shatters many marriages, though they may endure superficially.

Monotony has set in. Love-making may have become a dull and unimaginative act, performed without taste or consideration. On the other hand, the act of love may become shocking to the wife; this is a period of experimentation, when men tend to swap certain information in locker rooms.

It is also a period when the fantasy love lives of both husband and wife are full-blown. A woman may be disgusted at her thoughts when she watches a handsome young athlete; the male is less perturbed by his visions when he eyes girls in their summer dresses. It is a time when the husband is likely to wander, wistfully longing for a sense of achievement and the conviction that he is exceedingly male. Both are borne down by responsibilities—the wife with growing children and the husband with a developing career. Escape never looked more inviting. Not since they were in their teens has either member of the marriage been more immature in their lack of responsibility.

This period is normal. All new marriages should be aware that a time of restless seeking is coming. It can be weathered with the exercise of common sense, prudent control, humor, and a rich heaping of flattery. Some couples weather the white water by never speaking of it, clinging wordlessly in the small hours of the night, and waiting out the year with small talk until the seizure passes. Others wrestle with it openly, holding searing arguments and fervent conciliations, hurling their energies into some new joint occupation such as finishing the basement or playing golf. Sometimes, best of all, they laugh and moan, "Isn't this awful?" and hold tight to their marriage vows.

But many permit their marriage to be desecrated. They settle for separate lives under the same roof, which isn't a marriage at all. The husband becomes absorbed in his business and occasionally has affairs. The wife is a tyrant in her Home and School association or becomes blindly infatuated with building a wardrobe. Their conversations are monitored nothings for the sake of the children. Social occasions are opportunities to drink enough to establish an alibi for flirtations and other promiscuities.

When a marriage is about fifteen years old the husband's enjoyment requires more than the simple fulfillment of his youth. He now needs an affectionate response or else he is sickened. His wife must have warmth and tenderness in these years when passion is diminishing. This is the hardest time to remember he also wants to be intrigued and aroused. If his wife doesn't accomplish this, someone else may.

If the wife has failed to understand the changing quality of love-making over the years and if the gap that began in the tenth year has never been mended, another crisis will occur at the twenty-fifth anniversary. The couple is now middle-aged and the children grown and gone. They may decide to go on living together because the forces of habit are so strong, but many of them divorce. Protest as she may, the woman can no longer do anything to save her marriage. She goes adrift in a cold and lonely sea. The time to fight to save a marriage is before the tenth year.

I am often asked, "How long does the sex life of a woman last?" My answer is, "It never stops." I urge older women who are experiencing some pain during love-making to see their doctors immediately. This is known technically as senile change, although it can occur in a comparatively young woman who has had some repair work done after her children were born or a woman who has had no children.

The way to save a strained marriage, I advise my patients, is to start with the act of love. Here are the essentials of marriage in concentrated form—in one act are consideration, warmth, gaiety, charm, hunger, and ecstasy. In this small kingdom a woman can heal the wounds caused by contempt and indifference. She is a fool if she ignores this weapon provided her by nature.

The commitment of marriage is more than a living together until death do you part. It is more than a compromise in which both parties make the best of a situation fraught with dullness. I believe the marriage ceremony commits all women to understand the physical and emotional needs of their husbands. In the giving of their thoughtfulness, tenderness, and responsiveness, they can live all their lives in a golden glow. They will be needed and cherished. Few women would ask for more.

CHAPTER FIVE

An Open Letter to Husbands

ONE evening, about a year after I had started writing the series of articles for *Chatelaine,* I was approached by an agitated man at a party.

"Dr. Hilliard," he said, "I've been wanting to talk to you. My marriage is in terrible shape; we aren't getting along at all. We've got three children and we don't want to have to separate, for their sake. Won't you please help us?"

"Well," I began uncomfortably, "I'm afraid I can't. . . ."

"Please," he begged. "It will only take a minute. I'll get my wife and you tell her what she's doing wrong."

I have been pondering this conversation for some time and I wonder if I may not have been partly to blame for the man's conviction that only his wife could be at fault when his marriage soured. I have stated many times, and I still believe it, that the burden of creating a happy marriage falls mainly on the wife. A man's life is much more difficult than a woman's, full of the groaning strain of responsibility and the lonely and often fruitless search for pride in himself. A cheerful and contented woman at home, even one who must often pretend gaiety, gives a man enough confidence to believe he can lick the universe. I'm certain that the woman who enriches her husband with her admiration and her ready response gets her reward on earth, from her husband.

But the building of a solid marriage is not entirely a female function. Some husbands give nothing to a marriage but bread, which sustains life but not joy. Some husbands make it utterly impossible for even a lighthearted woman to greet them with a smile. Many husbands are haphazard in their observance of the commandment covering adultery and look for the solution of their failures in the ready acquiescence of a lonely and frustrated woman to whom they do not happen to be married. A few husbands seem to believe that a wife needs only a new vacuum cleaner for a full, rich life; it's like giving a sick child a new doll in the smug conviction that it will cure her pneumonia. Most tragically of all, thousands of husbands never understand the needs of their wives in love-making.

I've heard a good deal about husbands—enough to form some well-grounded conclusions. Sometimes, as a wife twists her way through an explanation of her troubles, dropping irrelevancies with her tears, I get a much better picture of her husband than I do of her.

In reflection, it seems to me that much of the difficulty with husbands begins with the problems of adolescent boys. A primary mistake is that the only female value a boy recognizes is early-blooming beauty. In this he often is abetted by his father, who congratulates him effusively when he dates a pretty girl and rattles his newspaper when he announces that he is attracted by a plain one. Many teen-age boys therefore have but one standard in judging a girl's character and intelligence: Is she a dish?

Dating is a coupling designed to help young men and women decide on the qualities they want in a partner for marriage. Too many boys play this dead-serious game as if they were judges at an Atlantic City beauty contest. It's like a scientist searching for a cancer cure and aiming all his research at locating one that is pink. It leads to marriages of strangers, both physically attractive in the wedding picture and both galloping for a fall. Here is an area where fathers can teach by example: as long as their faces light up like pinball machines registering TILT every time a lush female undulates by, they cannot expect their sons to develop a very mature appreciation of women.

Parents also need to be aware of the compelling need that adolescent boys have to prove their manhood, by one means or another. The coming-of-age rites in North America differ in every neighborhood. Sometimes a boy can prove himself by risking his neck in a high dive off a bridge, or scoring a touchdown while draped with enemy tacklers, or in driving a battered convertible at a speed approaching sound. Most of the so-called wildness of youth is the real necessity to demonstrate daring in order to satisfy the developing sensual appetite.

The phoniest proof of manhood that can be devised—the physical act of love—is demanded by some teen-age societies. A boy believes he must prove himself manly by succeeding with the town child-harlot or with some older woman. There is real danger inherent in this. The boy certainly will be frightened and awkward; he may also be too fastidious. The chances that he will fail in this initial attempt are very good, and such failure will terrify him. He may even suffer from impotence afterward —psychological impotence is a demonstrable fact. Parents must help their sons find a more acceptable method of proving themselves. A boy must appreciate that the act of love is outgoing and can only be debased, possibly forever, by trying to make it a manly achievement.

A growing boy must learn to discipline his sex drive. Puberty, in a male, crowds his mind with fuzzy imaginings, purples his stag conversations with lusty lies and causes him to push intimacies with girls to the limit of acceptance—and sometimes, in the urgency of passion, a bit beyond. Parents, who know so well how to administer a boy's allowance, how to regulate his homework, how to get him to remember to tuck in his shirt, are prone to mishandle the problem of his sexual urges. Some parents assume the situation is adequately covered with a curt "Don't," which is disastrously unhelpful. Others carefully explain that a boy and girl have the power to start a life, a power too magnificent to be used casually as a toy.

This is better, but it also falls short. From the number of unmarried teen-age mothers I have seen, quite a few high-school boys have evolved zany methods that they are certain will prevent pregnancy. Their practices horrify doctors; they are as imaginative as they are ineffective. Among the saddest words in the English language are surely, "Don't worry, dear, I can take care of you." For many years I lectured a mixed audience of college students on the subject of preparing for marriage. Whenever I commented on the widespread summer murmurings of "Don't worry," that led so often to babies in the spring, I noticed an uneasy ripple of recognition pass through the group.

Adolescent boys need to be impressed with more than the knowledge that they are able to start life. Each boy needs to know that promiscuity is habit forming and can make a shambles of his adult life. Promiscuity, in fact, is a mass of contradictions. It is not the indulgence of confident, capable men but of men who have been defeated; it doesn't attract men of achievement, but only men looking for achievement; it has no charm for a strong man, but only for a weak one.

Promiscuity is in itself weakening. It destroys, much as a narcotic does, and for the same reason. It has the identical effect of blacking out disappointments and making a man feel nine feet tall—and it has the same hangover the next day, with the disappointments still unsolved and the man even smaller and less inclined to cope with them. He reasons like a fool: maybe next time the effect will be lasting, next time with a different girl. It never is. The lack is not in the girls, it's in him. The promiscuous man is not oversexed at all; he's undersexed. He's not looking to give something, but to get it.

This desolate pattern can be set in adolescence. A boy must not indulge himself in his youth if he wants to be a coherent, secure adult. He might keep in mind that gluttons don't enjoy the taste of food.

An adolescent boy can check on his own incipient gluttony by means of a bit of introspection. When he contemplates his date for the evening, is he considering the reward he will get for his investment? Does he choose his date for the movie with his mind on getting the most return? This is downright immoral. No boy should expect a girl to pay for her evening's entertainment by permitting petting.

A youth should also understand his own biology. Throughout the life span, the male urge for sex is much stronger than the female. It is the boy who will light the bonfire. The best prevention of burns is to make certain that the location prohibits the fire getting out of hand. A good place for the good-night kiss is on the girl's doorstep; the boy goes home pleasantly tingling. The worst place is a parked car on a lonely road; he may go home full of terror and guilt.

It seems to me curious that an admission of virginity is considered highly desirable in a woman, but slightly pathetic and effeminate in a man. For this unreasonable reason, many men approaching marriage are ashamed to ask for advice. When he is joshed ribaldly by his friends, the prospective bridegroom responds with a lewd chuckle designed to give the impression that he has been in and out of women's bedrooms since he was twelve. Alone with his thoughts afterward, he is shaken by panic. He doesn't want to appear clumsy on his wedding night, but he can't ask for help without admitting he is inexperienced. He is stuck in the cage men build for themselves with their strutting conviction that men are naturally skilled lovers. They're not. I've consoled several thousand brides who could, but won't, testify to this.

Men approaching marriage need advice just as urgently as do brides. They need to know that adroit love-making is an educated act, the result of experience. First attempts are almost certain to be ludicrous disasters and dignity will be an impossible garment to wear. A honeymoon needs easy laughter to mend its tattered technique. Almost every man goes through an early stage in his love-making when the duration nature allows him is far too short. This should not cause concern and humiliation; it's perfectly normal.

Embarrassment is common among bridegrooms, but overanxiety is even more prevalent. These two defeat coordination and judgment; humor is the only weapon against them. The overanxiety springs from the man's feeling that the success or failure of the physical union will depend entirely on him. He doesn't realize that the act of love is a communication, not his gift exclusively. Both partners bring different gifts to this communication and derive from it different values. It is paramount that the man understand that a woman doesn't enjoy love in the same way he does. His satisfaction is constant and fairly simple to achieve; her delight varies each time and is complex. A woman's enjoyment is derived from the tenderness of the prelude to love and not as frequently from the act itself. A man who insists that a woman's response be the same as his own is forcing pretense on her.

The premarital experience is entirely the prelude to love—exciting, thrilling and stimulating to the woman. After marriage many husbands feel that this wooing is no longer necessary and that their wives will have pleasure in the simple, unadorned act itself. This is wrong. To ensure his bride's happiness, and circuitously his own pride in himself as a lover, a man must play it her way. The physical love of woman springs from total stimulation.

The other part of the act of love for women is the afterglow, when a woman wants to be cherished and a man has a tendency to turn away. The man must control his impulse to reject her after the storm, because a woman needs gentleness and reassuring warmth. Lovemaking requires the good manners of consideration and a great deal of respect for the separate needs of man and woman. The modern insistence on the female orgasm is a serious mistake that mars many unions.

The time for love-making is often more of a problem than many couples realize—"I feel so fresh in the early morning," a husband laments, "and you can't speak to my wife until she's had her coffee. She begins to pick up about midnight when I'm dead. What should we do?" Try a holiday weekend, try various times and places. Experiment and be ready to give in to each other from time to time.

Grandpa had it easier—Grandma wasn't even expected to like intercourse.

The most exciting part of my routine in the delivery room, next to the moment of birth itself, has always been phoning the father. Early in my practice I would be so anxious to assure him that his wife was fine and that his baby was normal that I would forget entirely

58

to notice the sex of the infant. I learned rapidly that this is an important detail for fathers and I finally formed the habit of writing the sex on a slip of paper before I phoned, so I wouldn't forget. I'll never forget the night I phoned a father and said, trying not to sound as exhausted as I felt, "Mr. Jones, you've got a wonderful new daughter!"

"That can't be mine. You're wrong," he said firmly. "I'm having a son."

When a couple is having a first baby I always find the husband taut and disheveled, pacing the halls. He waits until the birth is over, looks vaguely at his red-faced offspring, and hurries to his wife's bedside to stroke her face and whisper in her ear. This is a great moment in both their lives, unforgettable and charged with choking emotion.

When the next baby is born the father brings his wife into the hospital and asks me casually, "How long do you think it will take, Doctor?"

He then departs, and when the birth is over I phone him. "Tell my wife," he says before hanging up, "I'll be in to see her in the morning on my way to work."

Maybe I'm being fatuously romantic, but I don't think so. I think every father belongs beside his wife, whether she returns from the delivery room after her first or her tenth baby. Birth is an experience that doesn't become inconsequential with repetition. Women suffer from depression after even an easy birth; they need the comfort of their husbands and I haven't much regard for the men who place more value on an uninterrupted night's sleep than on their wives' contentment.

I wish men weren't so concerned about their virility. They place enormous value on their ability to reproduce, an asset that at best is only normal and expected, and are shattered if some doctor informs them that they are sterile. In approximately 60 per cent of the cases where the marriage has failed to produce a child, the male is at fault. But many men refuse to be examined at all, because they cannot face even the possibility that they might be the cause. Sometimes, unfortunately, such men refuse to permit the adoption of a child; it seems to them a public admission of failure.

I can't criticize husbands in general without praising them as well. Husbands, even those with no previous exhibitions of thoughtfulness, are wonderfully gentle when their wives become ill. If the limits that a doctor places on the time that both must be celibate are reasonable, husbands seem to lose all sexual desire and are relaxed and gentle with their wives. This resource of understanding is one on which doctors have come to rely. Some phenomenons have even been observed: philanderers, in an excess of zealous co-operation when their wives are ill, will sever relations with all other women as well.

This brings me to the graceless subject of adultery. Some men are promiscuous in their youth and haven't the sense or the control to stop themselves later. These are the child-men, searching for new toys. Marriage has no meaning for them because they lack the maturity to appreciate its values. As they grow older, their conquests become shabbier and their delusions about themselves must become correspondingly greater. It's a tawdry, pitiable existence with a certain ending: sans family, sans dignity, sans all.

But most men, I suspect, contemplate a small amount of adultery and this happens usually after they have been married about ten years. At this period all of the forces that tempt a man to wander have ripened. First, his job is not as time consuming as it was in the early years and his income is sufficient to support his fancies. Second, his love-making with his wife has fallen into a pattern, monotonous and predictable for them both. And most important of all, the man has the feeling that the interesting part of his life is over. He has found his own limitations and the limitations of his occupation. His body is beginning to thicken and his hair to thin. He badly needs a sense of adventure, and at this propitious moment he catches an adoring look on his secretary's face or else a former girl friend turns up, single and bright of eye.

If he permits himself to gallop gaily into an extra-marital relationship, he is going to have problems. Philandering is extremely expensive and is bound to strain his financial resources. It also requires a great deal of time, some of which he may have preferred to spend with his children or on the golf course. Little gentleman that he is, he is greatly concerned with secrecy: he doesn't want to hurt his wife's feelings. As his mistress becomes more familiar, she becomes more demanding. She has him at her mercy, and she knows it. He worries and writhes and finally, if he's lucky, he escapes her. He sighs with relief—and starts over again with another woman.

Some men go from woman to woman for years, despite the discovery they make at the beginning that their own climax is exactly the same every time. The philanderings have only the advantage of the excitement of pursuit and the satisfaction of victory. They have the disadvantage of splitting a man's life; one half accepted and comfortable, and the other half illicit and degrading. He suffers a similar split in his inner self, one side of him searching for support for his ego and the other rejecting the affections of an easily won woman as false.

Instead of an affair, a man who is beginning to feel restless needs a substitute adventure. Membership in a spirited service club provides this for some men, so does a hunting or fishing trip at regular intervals. Some men work off the cravings of these moody years by heading community campaigns, building with their own hands extensions on their homes or rock gardens. All of these are effective, but the most beneficial method of all in order to avoid the furtiveness of an affair is to renew the enchantment of love-making within the marriage. No marriage bed needs to suffer the curse of uniformity; to be successful, love-making needs ingenuity, zest, and cherishing.

Eventually in a man's life he is going to experience a slackening in his sexual desire. Sometimes this happens prematurely when a man exhausts himself with overwork or else is constantly excited by some diversion, such as following the horses or stock market. It's foolish to blame the impotency on the wife; some men do this and set out briskly to find another woman, only to find that the situation is unchanged. Both work and excitement are enormous consumers of a man's energy; the other great consumer is sex. A man must ration his energy to have some left over at the end of the day.

Whether the loss of desire is premature and curable, as in the cases I have just mentioned, or the incurable process of aging, a man is invariably aghast when his virility begins to fade. A man places virility at the pinnacle of all his achievements and he is devastated as it begins to slip away. The only thing comparable in women is the importance they place on their breasts. Many middle-aged men react violently to the problem of their dwindling virility. They pretend to have Gargantuan appetites for sex and tell extraordinary lies to one another. They favor the rawest form of humor, girlie shows and bottom pinching. They leer at young women and sing loudly at parties the explicit lyrics of lecherous songs. They are altogether pathetic, and they fool no one.

A man must accept the fact that his loss of sexual desire is part of the pattern of life. These are difficult years for him, years that have been described as a male menopause. He is oppressed by his languishing virility, disturbed by his past mistakes and the glories he missed, and frightened by the inscrutable future, when his finances may be inadequate. It is a time when he will be nervous and irritable and sunken with self-pity.

Because of the cyclic life of menstruation, women are accustomed to having periods of irritability and depression; men are not. A man at this time of life is inclined to blame this decline on his health. He goes from doctor to doctor, complaining of twinges and aches that he would never have noticed as a young man. He feels his heart after every exertion and notes the ages of the men in obituary columns who died of heart attacks. He treats his body as if it was a rare jewel, feeds it carefully, and rests it well.

The first thing he ought to do to recover from all of this is take a good look at himself. He's comical enough to give himself at least a good chuckle, and maybe even a belly laugh. He's no Romeo, it's true, but he has his self-respect, the esteem of his community, the steady affection of his wife, the friendship of his children and the uncritical adoration of his grandchildren. He can live to the end of his days in serenity, having accomplished much in getting through a lifetime with his integrity intact.

He's a lucky man. The light in his eye is laughter.

CHAPTER SIX

What Women Don't Know About Being Female

A SUNDAY-SCHOOL teacher, unmarried and sedate of appearance, came into my office one afternoon with some symptoms of headaches and sleeplessness. She talked around the subject for quite a while and then began telling me about a man she had been seeing lately. "Then he took me to the theater . . ." she was saying. My attention wandered; it was spring, the Stanley Cup play-offs were just ending, Gieseking had given a Beethoven concert at Massey Hall the night before, and the fishing season was about to open.

Suddenly I became aware that my patient had stopped talking. I was dismayed because I hadn't heard a word for some time. I decided to try to bluff. "Well, then he asked you to his apartment. What did you say to him?"

The woman's jaw dropped open. "How did you know?" she exclaimed. "I was just going to tell you that!"

I apologized for spoiling her story. I couldn't tell her that I've heard a myriad variations of the same tale and they all end the same way. No matter who tells it, from an adolescent to a matron, plain or pretty, virgin or wanton, there comes the moment when some man asks them to his apartment, or to a hotel room. I am no longer as amazed as I used to be that each of these women appears to believe the man's invitation was an extraordinary and astonishing development akin to the sky falling down.

They are victims of what I believe is a woman's greatest mistake: underestimating what I shall term her biology. Creation has gone to considerable trouble to make her female, to grant her certain glands and desires and an aura to enhance her in the eyes of males, and then she is full of innocent surprise and wonderment when these attributes demonstrate that they are in working order.

"I'm not that kind of girl," they explain to me. This is outrageous nonsense. Except for a statistical handful who have abnormally low metabolisms, everybody is that kind of girl.

From the day she is born until she dies a woman

must live with her gender. Some women have the impression that being female is a bundle of tricks, such as squealing at mice, being poor at arithmetic, tears, perfume behind the ears, and an attitude of fragil wonder in the face of an abstract like international justice or a concrete like garbage-collection day.

Femaleness, as any doctor will tell you, is savage. Woman is equipped with a reproductive system which, even if she never uses it, dominates her fiber. It has vicious power that can leap out of control without the slightest warning, while a man and a woman share a companionable chuckle or happen to touch hands. In the time it takes to blink, they have reached a point of no return. The mechanism of woman can also be triggered unexpectedly by the low moan of a crooner, by a summer sky full of stars, by the sight of a man's hands working with metal, or even by fog collecting around a street light. Involuntarily the woman is twisted inside with anguish and longing. It's her biology again. Any pretense that this force does not exist is as bizarre and illogical as pretending there is no atom bomb.

When I was a younger doctor, caring for unmarried women who were about to have babies, I used to ask the more intelligent and sensible of them, "How could this have happened to you?" The girl would answer simply. "I couldn't help myself," and I used to turn away skeptically. I believed then, as almost all women do, that a woman controlled the quality of her relationship with a man. If it became intimate, I reasoned, it was because she deliberately chose to let it happen.

This just isn't true. I'm wiser now and I realize that there can come a moment between a man and a woman when control and judgment are impossible. An easy companionship traveling at about ten miles an hour can shift to a blinding passion going a hundred miles an hour without any warning, soundlessly. In a moment, by a glandular whim that makes a mockery of conscience and discretion, the self-respect and composure of the woman may be eternally damaged.

A woman's first protection against this betrayal is to appreciate that the speed-up of her emotions is not only possible, but natural and normal. Her best defense is to have no confidence at all in her ability to say nay at the appropriate moment. The belief that any woman can coolly decide to halt love-making at some point before she is wholly committed is a tiger trap devised by the romantics. Negatives during an ecstatic embrace are for Jane Austen's paper heroines and not for a lady of flesh and blood.

For this reason women have to safeguard themselves with a standard of conduct that may seem quaint and archaic. The freedom a modern girl allows herself is a delusion—it gives her no freedom of choice whatsoever.

I cannot be so unrealistic as to suggest that teen-agers, for example, should never kiss; few parents even attempt to impose such an unnatural restriction on their children. But not enough mothers warn their daughters that kissing is intended by nature to be an appetizer, not an entire meal. Some parents seem to believe, mistakenly, that tumults of emotion happen only to adults.

I've been called upon occasionally to advise girls of high-school age. My rules are based not so much on avoiding social censure as on avoiding personal torment. I'm not concerned with the community's approval so much as the youngster's own opinion of herself. A promiscuous youngster is ravaged by her own bitter conscience; her greatest tragedy isn't the loss of her reputation—it's the loss of her self-respect.

For this reason I suggest that teen-age girls shouldn't pet with a casual date, because such dates usually have little sense of responsibility and consideration. Teen-agers shouldn't pet in automobiles, where there is no possibility of outside help. They shouldn't pet as a means of putting in time, just because they have nothing better to do and are looking for thrills. Human passion is no toy to be used whenever the couple is bored. A girl should never permit petting out of a sense of obligation.

Some youngsters, however, do have a deep and true feeling for one another that transcends the frivolous attachments of their friends. This relationship, rare in teen-agers because it is so mature, can be distinguished by its quality of affection. Affection is the enduring element in any man-woman association. Passion is a bonfire that soon burns itself out, but affection can last a lifetime. It frightens me that movies, popular songs, and television constantly portray only the passion side of human love, giving our adolescents the false impression that this is love in its entirety. Nothing could be more wrong; real love is mainly affection.

These same rules still hold for a college girl or one beginning to work in an office, factory or store. Some new situations, however, have been added. Visiting the man's hotel room or apartment alone is like playing with loaded dice—you lose every time.

My most important piece of advice for any woman is to play in her own league. I mean this in a variety of ways: a young girl shouldn't go with an older man, a secretary with her boss, a naïve woman with a sophisticate, a sheltered youngster with a hoodlum in a windbreaker. Those who do are sure to be hurt.

I want to deal mainly with the problems of an unmarried woman in this chapter, but I must digress to point out that married women can also be shattered if they fail to respect the power of their biology. Wives, trusting in the myth that "nothing can happen" because they are with a good friend or neighbor, sometimes seek to nourish their egos with easy kisses and embraces. They can set in motion a violence beyond control. I know. I have delivered the children born of these affairs and listened to the details of their divorces. "I couldn't help myself," they wail. I believe them, but they could have prevented the catastrophe if they hadn't agreed to switch husbands for the drive back to town or to inspect the back nine in the moonlight.

I'll never understand how "this thing is bigger than both of us" ever got to be a comedy.

A few years ago, a patient of mine came into Women's College Hospital to have her second baby. Her best friend, she told me, was taking a two-week vacation in order to care for her first child and prepare meals for her husband. "A dandy arrangement," I thought to myself, "just dandy." A few months later my heartbroken patient had instigated divorce proceedings, naming her best friend as corespondent.

"How could she? How could she?" sobbed my patient. I sympathized but I still feel she had brought the situation on herself by putting her husband and friend in an intimate arrangement where normal restraint was difficult. As a doctor I don't believe there is such a thing as a platonic relationship between a man and a woman who are alone together a good deal.

Much of my practice has been with women who have been labeled career women. Most of them are highly intelligent, charming, and attractive; most of them are also unmarried.

A hundred or more of them have whispered to me, "Doctor, I'm not married and it doesn't look as though I'm going to be married. What do I do with sex?"

To me it is as ridiculous as asking what to do with lungs. The sex drive is as natural a part of a woman as the need for oxygen. She uses her lungs for breathing and her sex drive, properly channeled, for enriching her life.

The first move is to stop being selfish and self-centered. A woman who feels unwanted is bound to get into trouble; she's looking for it. The unmarried woman has to face up to herself and her life. She's got to stop expecting life to be fair. Life isn't meant to be that way at all. Life doesn't owe her a handsome adoring husband and two beautiful children full of bright sayings—life owes her nothing. She has to reorganize her thinking so that she can be grateful for the good things that happen to her and work her way through the bad things without a sense of defeat.

This is the bitter, desperate adjustment that the single woman has to make. Nothing will again be as painful as the moment she realizes that she will live all her life alone; no moment will ever hurt so much. Once this is past she can begin to sort out her existence on the sound and sane basis of "This is how it is going to be," rather than the treacherous, doomed "This is what might happen tomorrow."

The first step is to build a home of her own that is a sanctuary, not just a place to hang her beret. Just like the married woman, she must learn to be a good housekeeper, a tasteful interior decorator, an imaginative cook. It is very hard, in the beginning, to be alone. It's a good idea to start a music collection to help fill the emptiness and a better idea to find a group activity, such as a business girls' club or a badminton club, where an unescorted girl doesn't feel out of place.

I might add that when the unmarried girl, sitting alone in her apartment through a soft spring night, feels most forlorn and lonely she can meditate on the lot of the many married women who are also alone that night because their husbands are traveling, or working late, or out with the boys, or philandering.

A married woman doctor on our staff had been looking exhausted for months. I finally asked what was the matter. "I've had trouble keeping a housekeeper," she explained, "so I have a lot of housework to do when I get home. Our children are having difficulties in school so they need a lot of help and my husband likes to entertain. I haven't drawn a carefree breath in two years."

"Don't tell me," I suggested, "tell all our unmarried women doctors who are moping around the hospital being sorry for themselves and envying you."

It's curious how many unmarried women have the impression that a marriage license automatically assures an idyllic existence. I sometimes suspect that the myth is kept alive by married women who regard the Paris-copy clothes of their unmarried sisters, examine the un-scratched coffee tables, listen to the tales of bus trips to Mexico and opening nights at the theater, and then remark blandly: "Isn't it a shame you aren't married. You poor dear!"

The unmarried girl is wise to plan her off-duty pleas-ure with groups to which she herself naturally belongs—badminton and tennis, skiing weekends, church groups, creative arts—and make new friends, both male and female. She must never cling to her old friends who have married and of necessity have formed other en-tertainment routines which include husbands. There is no point in her flattening her nose against the candy-store window, and she's out of place at a gathering of married couples. As her friends marry, her relationship with them must continue in the area that is unchanged by the marriage—luncheons, shopping trips, women's club activities. Otherwise the married woman's and un-married woman's lives are too different; they can only, unwittingly, hurt one another.

If the unmarried girl is fortunate enough to find another girl her own age with whom she can share her interest in art galleries or books, they are wise to consider sharing an apartment. Both girls, through their mutual respect and affection, can help one an-other through the lonely patches of their lives. The essential of such a relationship is that neither girl tries to dominate the other and that both are free to go on about their work unchanged. I've always considered it a dreadful wrong to impose your personality and opinions on any other person, in a friendship or a marriage. I was once asked for my definition of living in sin. It's this: Any two people living together while one dominates and tyrannizes the other are, to me, living in sin.

This takes care of the surface details of the single woman's existence. We come now to the difficult and complex area of her biology. Some women have met this problem with the ingenious hallucination that it doesn't exist. They keep a tidy brain. "You aren't married," they remind themselves, "so you don't even think about such things." They withdraw and become gray shadows, living gray-shadow lives that are utter wastes.

The sex drive of the normal woman is capable of giving her great radiance. It's the force within her that makes her gentle with children; it's a power than can knock the cover off a golf ball or take her straight down an almost perpendicular ski trail; it's part of the passion she feels when an animal is mistreated; it's in the understanding she can give another human being who is desperately lonely.

It can also make her the most miserable of women. I recommend a policy of prevention in order to lessen the shattering effect of desire. If walking in the darkness makes a woman ache inside, then she should stick to daylight for her strolls. New Orleans jazz has a primitive tom-tom rhythm that does a single woman's peace of mind no good. Tchaikovsky wrote some mood music for two—and despair music for one. It's masochistic to listen to music that is disturbing.

The single woman must also avoid involvement in casual dates. "Sleeping around," as casual love-making is known in the vernacular, is destructive for a woman. Even if she avoids the formidable threat of pregnancy, her physiological pattern is shocked and mortified by the callous emptiness of promiscuity. A woman gets no

71

real fulfillment in such flippant attachments; she is degraded and her spirit suffers terrible damage.

The human needs that a woman cannot do without don't include passion at all. They are affection, a sense of achievement, status, and security. These four are the permanent necessities; the need for sex is a transient longing. The body can withstand a lack of physical love-making; the spirit can't withstand a lack of affection, achievement, status, or security. I can't assure any woman that the desire for physical love is a light whim of the moment that will pass painlessly; it's a deep and terrible torment that can be met only by exhausting physical activity, by plunging into a professional challenge that is almost too big to handle, by volunteering for some demanding charitable work.

I've discovered, over an adult lifetime of looking at this problem, that each age group of the unmarried girl has its own distinguishing characteristic and must be dealt with separately. With girls in their twenties, the most common disaster is that an older man exploits the girl's admiration of him. Too often in offices, young secretaries come to adore worldly, urbane, middle-aged bosses. For a man of experience it is a simple matter to charm the girl into a hotel suite. This is the vilest crime a man can commit against the woman and often destroys her chance to marry. No woman is truly astonished when such a proposal is made; the man's purpose is shown in advance by the tone of his voice, by his special interest, by not very paternal pats on the head. My advice to any girl aware of the possibility is to run. In order to avoid what is otherwise inevitable and dangerous, she must leave her job immediately.

A woman in her thirties has a dwindling chance of marrying. She has realized the path her life is taking—and it never looked more unpalatable. Her friends have small children and she is tortured by the knowledge that she will never hold her own baby. She is calling herself a bachelor girl, but she knows the synonym is old maid. At this point in her life passion is going to sear her to the bone. She is bound to fall in love and her love is almost sure to be married, that's how fate always seems to set it up.

"I'm thinking of having an affair—with a married man," a patient of mine once told me bluntly. I suspect she was waiting for me to express horror and fan myself rapidly with a medical journal.

"Are you truly in love," I asked her, "or is this a physical need?"

"I love him desperately," she cried.

I told her what it means in a community to have an affair with a man. She would have to give up all her friends and clubs and go into a social and moral retreat; she would have to lie to her relatives in an attempt, usually unsuccessful, to keep the knowledge from them; she would have to be strong enough to accept that she was a part-time, illicit wife. She would have to face the knowledge that a real wife, bearing children and welcomed by society, existed elsewhere. Finally, she would have to begin the affair knowing it will end in three to five years, leaving her alone. My patient had thought her way through all these separate agonies and she was prepared for them all.

"Come back to me in three years when it is over," I told her. "I'll try to help you put your life back together again."

She came back, quieter, drained and passive, almost exactly three years later. The affair had ended and she was paying a bleak price. She had been standing still, treading water, for those years and her friends had passed her and become strangers. She would be a long time catching up.

An affair is a relationship that doesn't fit into any pattern that our society accepts. It is furtive and without the stamp of approval every woman fervently wants from her friends. She loses caste and has a sense of sickness in her soul. Yet if a woman understands the sacrifice that will be demanded of her and is deeply in love, I cannot in any sincerity condemn the relationship. If tarnish can be avoided, and disillusionment and doubt, she will have a brief love to cherish and remember all her life. Such a love must be held gently and relinquished, when the time comes, without tears.

Most women in their thirties are preoccupied with a search for status. They feel disgraced if they have to arrive at a party with another girl, exit from movies alone, play cards only with women. They are willing to barter anything in order to have a male escort. It is the blight of our civilization that so much importance has been placed on a male attendant. Every day of every week a girl is hounded by a stream of advertising—what lipstick to use, what cream will lure a man or hold him. Beauty has only one object, to trap the male. Because of this, the unmarried girl becomes part of a misshapen pattern; she's a party girl, available without dignity or grace, or else she dates younger, immature men who are looking for a mother. A recognizable type of foppish, weak man makes a practice of dating clever, restless women in their thirties. It is a sickening solution to the problem of a lack of escort, but too many women accept it greedily, gladly.

"But what do I do when I am in real distress because of desire?" I have been asked.

Read a mystery story, I answer. Visit a friend with five children under ten years of age. Take a very hot bath and plan your next vacation.

There is one special group which my heart yearns over, the young widows and divorcees, particularly the widows. These are single women who have known both worlds and so fit in nowhere. Also they seem to be considered fair game for any unscrupulous man. The fact that they have had sex experience enhances their

74

attractiveness. The same fundamental considerations hold here. The total happiness of the personality is at stake. To satisfy desire because of boredom, frustration, or defeat, destroys the little happiness that may grow again. I have seen so many widows, devastated by sorrow, starting out again to look after their homes and children, expecting that all desire is gone forever. Suddenly, with a rush, they may be enveloped in the old pattern of passion, aroused maybe by an old friend or even a new acquaintance. Their body betrays them. How can I convince them that this is a normal reaction that does not besmirch a beloved union? It is just an involuntary pattern that must be recognized to be understood and controlled. The sex pattern is always there, but no contentment can ever come from cherishing this moment.

It is hard for a woman to renounce motherhood, which many women feel is their birthright, but it is vital for the unmarried woman to make this stern decision. She must stop feeling that she deserves more out of life—life doesn't give any human what he or she deserves. No matter how sophisticated her set may be, it is impossible for the unmarried woman to consider having a baby. She can never live with the sense of continually hurting someone else, as such a child must be hurt.

As the single woman grows older she comes to a time when she wants the affection and admiration of younger people. Teachers seek the approval of their students, social workers involve themselves deeply in the problems of young people, office managers fondly direct the training of stenographers fresh from high school. The difficulty is often that the older woman is vicariously having her youth again; she is deeply wounded when the younger person becomes self-sufficient. This kind of domination, all too common, is bound to damage both women.

Women in their forties must guard against any tendency to attach themselves to a girl in order to starch a wilted ego.

The forty-year-old woman can make an extremely happy marriage—but it's not likely to happen. The great turmoils that spring from passion are almost finished and that terrible struggle is over. Life comes back into focus again and her job and friends look new and fresh. If she has been wise enough to join a group or lucky enough to be part of a close-knit community, this mass affection will keep her steady through her menopause. She will discover, when she looks at married women of her own age, that their adolescent children are keeping them in a continual state of apprehension and dismay. She may have a few pangs left over, but singleness no longer makes her so wretched.

Once the fifties have been reached and the menopause is passed, life can be clear and zestful. The unmarried woman finds that many of her married friends are now alone too, their marriages broken by divorce or death. Both women are in the same boat again, and the only things that are really important are financial security and the necessity of being needed.

If the woman is to arrive safely at this good time in her life with her conscience intact, much depends on how she has used her biology through the thirty years when it ravaged her contentment. If she has respected the enormity of its power to defeat her judgment, her biology will not have been able to harm her. If she has used its force to help others and herself, spreading its vitality and warmth among activities or friends who needed gentleness, then her life will have been rich and rewarding. Female biology can illuminate or desolate— but it can never be underestimated.

CHAPTER SEVEN

Stop Being "Just a Housewife"

~~~~~~

WHEN I was an adolescent in Morrisburg, Ontario, I used to sing a song that contained the line, "Men must work but women must weep." The rest of the song is gone from my memory, but that one line has been haunting me ever since. I believe that the most important thing I know about women is that women need not weep, but they must work.

I know exactly how most men and a lot of women will feel about my attitude. There is a prevailing image of womanhood, slightly plump in a cotton print dress, surrounded by adoring, golden-haired children as she bends over an oven door to take out a pan of biscuits. In this pink picture, the woman's face is brimming with contentment, tears of tender joy stand in her eyes and she is bathed in a glow of fulfilled femininity. She's wonderful all right, but she's no more real than the fantasy image millions of men have of themselves, exultant and virile, stripped to the waist in the sunshine, splitting rocks with Gargantuan strength.

People in our culture are too complicated to have more than fleeting moments of such acute sensation. Splitting rocks is unprofitable, making it impossible for a man to raise his family in a spacious neighborhood, and it also is incapable of satisfying his intelligence. The desire to be half naked and muscular must give way to the reality of a pallid face and a gray-flannel figure crouched over a desk.

Similarly, women cannot perpetually achieve the ideal state of enriched motherhood. Motherhood, in reality, turns out to be a state with well-spaced-out rewards—the thrill of nursing a baby, the look on a small child's face when he is comforted after a fall, a remark of a school-going child that shows understanding and warmth, a shared laugh with an adolescent, a first date, a graduation, a wedding, a grandchild. In between are periods of monotony and a feeling of stagnation.

Much of the fault for the current mood of nameless longing that is sweeping modern housewives is to be found in their so-called blessings. Women no longer weave their own cloth, make their own soap, put down a cellarful of preserves. Consider the mid-twentieth-century woman: She is alone in her house, miles from her family and the friends of her childhood; her work has been simplified to the glorious point where she can keep her house glittering in two hours a day; she stares into her own thoughts while the refrigerator clicks on, the oven bakes the prepared cake mix, and her children play in denims that need no ironing. She has married young, earlier every year in Canada according to the statistics. She's strong, intelligent and responsible. She sits with a cigarette in her fingers and feels futile. I say she needs to work.

I'd like to emphasize immediately that I have several convictions about why women should work, and none of them include money. To take a job merely for the sake of a pay check is a spiritless and degrading business. It's the blight of our times—men and women working at gray, loathed occupations purely for the sake of income. It flies in the face of the human necessity to take pride in a job, and the repetitious agony of an occupation that gives no satisfaction can lead to mental or physical breakdown. I am shocked by the number of our adolescents who take light, aimless jobs when they leave school, putting in time until marriage. College girls wait on tables at summer resorts in order to purchase cashmere sweaters. Young married women stand behind counters in department stores so they can pay the next installment on the refrigerator—and when that is paid off they'll make a down payment on a clothes dryer. These women have settled on a materialistic standard, filling their closets with clothes and their kitchens with electric appliances. They don't realize that their vitality is turning to cold ashes and their spirit is impoverished.

Women must work; all women must work. There is no place in our society for an indolent woman. But as a doctor I am certain that it is good health therapy to work and that women must work for values other than purely economic. Women need to work to gain confidence. Women need to work in order to know achievement. Women need to work to escape loneliness. Women need to work to avoid feeling like demihumans, half woman and half sloth.

Work, as I mean it, includes any activity that fulfills these needs. It includes hospitality, a complicated and rewarding occupation. It includes active membership in an organization that is performing a vital function in the community. It includes part-time work in a dress shop, if the woman is stimulated by handling new clothes and meeting a variety of people. It includes full-time work at a job that challenges and delights her, providing she has some enthusiasm and glow left over afterward for her home.

I am not speaking of the unmarried woman, who will work all her adult life. She too needs to choose an occupation in which she can find some expression of her personality, whether it be chatting with people over a bakeshop counter or peering through a microscope in search of a cure for cancer. But she is not fooled, as the married woman is fooled, into believing she can spend her whole life without acquiring a single skill.

This is the deep dark water under the thin ice of a

married woman's composure. Frittering away the scant years before she marries, she learns no trade. She comes to marriage with little ability beyond a certain flair for looking attractive in strong sunlight. On this house of cards she builds her self-assurance. She rises in the morning full of the delight of greeting her young loveliness in a mirror. But time won't hold still and this butterfly reaches her mid-thirties, when her children are almost independent and her one small talent is beginning to weather. The change in her appearance, which had counted for so much, makes her unsure. She is now ready, with her family nearly grown, to take part in the bustle outside her home, but she is newly timid and has no training. Unskilled occupations look wearying, unworthy, and dull; so she sits at home and becomes more despondent with each empty, wasted day.

One such woman came to me a few years ago. She was expensively dressed, given to tapping her fingers sharply on the arm of her chair, and full of vague symptoms of irritability, sleeplessness, and pains that changed location with each medical article she read. Both sons were in high school and her husband was absorbed in a business boom.

"You need to work," I told her.

"My husband is quite successful," she said coldly.

I shifted patiently. "I mean for your own sake," I explained. "What can you do?"

She butted her cigarette viciously. "Dr. Hilliard, I am thirty-six years old. I have two years of university education, sixteen years of marriage and a pretty good I.Q. I believe I am qualified to be a baby sitter."

I met an older version of the same woman not long ago. Her husband had died in his mid-fifties, and she was devastated.

"I know that self-pity isn't helping me," she commented sadly, "but I just sit in our pretty little home and cry."

"You'd better get a job," I said.

"A job!" she exclaimed. "I've never had a job in my life. What could I do?"

"Start down the street of the shopping district nearest you," I advised her, "and go into every store and ask for work until you find a job."

She took my suggestion and landed a job the next day in a dime store. Wrestling with the problems of learning to ring up sales and make change for the purchase of fifty-nine-cent wallets, she found new strength to accept her loneliness, and an awakened interest in people. She left that job for a better one and I haven't heard from her since. I suspect she is just fine.

It is time women took a good long look at their lives and realized that they will spend most of the years working. Most women realize that they will work before their marriage, but they don't know that this is only the beginning. If their husbands need to finish their educations, or become ill for a long period of time, the wives will have to work. If the marriage suffers either separation or divorce, both of which are increasingly common, the women go back to work. When the children are entering their teens, the women can easily fit a job into the home schedule. They'll be grandmothers in their forties, eagerly looking for something to fill their time. Women live longer than men, so it is likely that they'll spend the end of their lives, if they're lucky, working at a job that interests and delights them. In the long view, marriage and childbearing, although a desperate need, may be only an interlude in a woman's life.

Young people today approaching adulthood are betrayed by the ease with which they can make money. They need no skill at all and life is a lark. A teen-age girl with indifferent ability to type can make fifty dollars a week in an office and conserve all her animation for the coffee breaks and after-five dates. A boy I know made eighty dollars a week on a road-construction gang, guiding traffic with a red flag. He had the wit to be ashamed of himself, but his savings paid his first-year medical-school fees.

With jobs so easy to come by, many adolescent girls are fooled into believing that only the salary is an important factor in choosing an occupation. The jobs that require training and education, such as nursing and teaching, have little charm. They'll be marrying soon, they figure, so why bother?

Once a generation becomes adjusted to the notion that happiness varies in a direct ratio with dollars, desperate aberrations appear in its behavior. Last winter I had three mothers in three months come to me in their early pregnancies and tell me that they wanted their babies placed for adoption. These mothers were married, giving birth to legitimate babies. "Why give up your baby?" I asked.

"We can't afford to give this new baby the advantages it should have," the first mother told me. "We have two children now and we can't manage another."

"Do you think dancing lessons and brand-new snow suits are more important to a child than being with his own parents?" I inquired.

The mother was surprised. "Certainly," she answered.

I discovered to my sorrow that the adoption department of at least one children's aid society had to hire a special case worker to deal with the growing number of married couples who place their children for adoption. What has happened to our values if we can give up our babies because they strain the family budget? We pride ourselves on our Western way of life. "What shall it profit a man if he shall gain the whole world, and lose his own soul?"

This trend is evident in the mothers of teen-age girls who chat with pride about their daughters. "She's so pretty," they tell me gaily. "We belong to the country club because we want her to meet a nice crowd of people, and we try to keep her well dressed. She studied at the conservatory for years, but now she's more interested in badminton. She's having such a wonderful time!"

I wonder. Does she know what life is about, I think to myself. Does she have a core of serenity, derived from the knowledge that she is a capable, coherent human being? Is she prepared to live a long time and be able to respect herself most of those years? Or will she be bored for twenty or thirty years, turning her bitter venom on her children, her husband, her friendships that show signs of waning? Don't tell me your daughter can figure skate like Barbara Ann Scott. Tell me instead that she is generous and kind and that she has forethought enough to prepare herself for a creative vocation.

Men preparing themselves for a profession usually continue with their education after marriage, but a woman almost invariably stops her education at the first clang of the wedding bell. She believes, and she is dead wrong, that her training is of no importance. Many women tell themselves that they can always finish the course later, but later never happens. A middle-aged housewife is so rare in a university that she's newspaper copy. No woman should ever be concerned that her training as a teacher, a business-machine operator, or a dietician will ever be wasted when she marries. She will be using it, all right, and probably a lot sooner than she expects.

This brings us to the mothers of preschool children. Society agrees that babies and little children need their mother, an absolutely steady and reliable, loving woman. The mother who rushes her children through a dawn breakfast, nags them to hurry with their clothes so she can deposit them somewhere on her way to work and then returns, exhausted, in the early evening to prepare an ugly meal and send her children testily to bed is suffering a defeat on all fronts. She isn't a mother, wife, or woman. She's a wage earner and the $42.97 she gets every week, after deductions, cannot possibly justify what she is doing to herself.

It isn't the time she's away from the children, it's what happens in the hours she has them with her. I have known many mothers of preschool children who stayed home stubbornly to raise their small ones and managed to do as much harm as the working mother I have just described. These are the mothers who can never accept the estrangement of being a housewife. They remember the conviviality of the office they left for motherhood; lunching in laughter-filled restaurants; the lullaby relaxation of routine. They survey their present existence: an adult, spending an entire day in the company of a two-year-old, subject to the whims and demands of the child at erratic intervals, including the middle of the night; a highly skilled office worker, reduced to removing dust from the coffee table. She screams at her child, who is the cause of her plight, and afterward is racked by guilt. She soaks herself in radio and television to distract her mind, ordering her child to be quiet and go away. When she can't stand it any longer she goes out, leaving the child with some makeshift supervision. She prides herself on being a "good" mother because she isn't working; in her heart she must know she is a terrible mother.

This woman needs to work at something she can be proud of, in order to increase her importance to herself. It doesn't need to be a major occupation, lasting several hours a day, but it must be regular so she can look forward to it and plan the supervision of her child. I know of one woman in a northern Ontario city who discovered there was no kindergarten in the local schools. She campaigned, became a school-board trustee and led a movement to establish kindergartens. Another woman spends an afternoon a week teaching a cerebral-palsy victim of thirty-three how to read. I know another who became an expert gardener, growing hybrid roses, and another who, in a rebellion against depression one gray winter

84

day, started to scrape the finish off the dining-room table and eventually refinished with professional technique all the furniture in her house. All of these fulfill my requirements for working women, since they have the heavy remuneration of self-esteem and worth.

As the children grow older, I believe that they will gain by having a working mother. They can learn responsibility in no better way. There are, of course, two different ways of performing any assigned task. The twelve-year-old who is supposed to do the dinner dishes can feel abused—and be loquacious on the subject—and will try to avoid the chore at every opportunity. But if he understands that this is his contribution to his family and that he is an active participant in the machinery that makes the family work efficiently, there is rarely much difficulty.

Children have a great capacity for responsibility. Without any exception, mothers who have teen-age children and become pregnant tell me that their older children showed a solicitude and thoughtfulness that astounded their parents. "I didn't know they were capable of such understanding," the mother tells me. Those children are capable all right, and they and their parents both gain enormously in the discovery.

Although few mothers go back to a university to finish courses, a surprising number are taking night-school training in accounting or business machines, or refresher courses in some type of nursing or teaching. A woman social worker I know kept her hand in all through the years her three children were small, by intensive reading. She bought a small filing cabinet and kept all useful information in well-organized files. She went back to work, when her youngest child was ten, as knowledgeable as any fresh graduate.

Work is a wonderful antidote to the blues of menopause. This is a period when a woman's sense of uselessness is so acute that she can, literally, be driven to drink, dope, or mental illness. Her family is grown, her child-bearing years are ending, her husband often could do just as well with a hired housekeeper. If she has some consuming occupation, whether it is a study of four-teenth-century Chinese art or an office to manage, she isn't in much danger of being shattered by what is happening to her physiology.

Work is a great healer for a woman. A woman who discovered that her husband, much adored by their children, was chronically unfaithful, soothed her ravaged emotions by going back to work. Another woman, who was languishing in misery because she was sterile, pulled herself out of her own private pit by spending a morning a week bathing babies at an infants' home. The babies responded instantly to her loving gentleness in the midst of their institutional life; babies and woman helped one another through a bad time.

I'd like to add a special word for a woman trained in some profession, such as medicine or law, before her marriage. In our busy new country it is a tragic loss to have such a person disappear into the suburbs, and agonizingly difficult for such a woman to be content with peeling potatoes. Three quarters of the staff of Women's College Hospital where I work are married, and many of them have children. Quite a few women dentists and architects continue to work after their marriages. These women cannot possibly be motivated by money, I am delighted to say. The cost of housekeepers, the increased needs of their wardrobes, the whopping income tax they pay, at single-woman rates, all combine to reduce the possibility that a fondness for a bank account is a main factor. I know a woman doctor who last year, after paying her office upkeep, her secretary, her housekeeper, and her income tax, made six hundred dollars. She works, as happy, well-adjusted women everywhere work, because it satisfies her need to work, gives her joy in a job she loves.

Every Thursday night for twenty years I have been met by a gentle radiance in my living room. It uplifts my heart and dispels my fatigue. My staunch Scots friend has been there all day "bringing up" the shine, even of the window sills. That room is full of enduring integrity and devotion of one who loves to clean, and loves me too. She did not go to work to meet any deep psychological need, she went to work to feed her children. Now they are financially successful but she still works. It is the center of her life, for we are all dependent on her faithfulness. I pay this special tribute to all those cheerful women who do hard rough work, so that the mother, the business and professional woman can be refreshed and do a better job. I hope they see their reward and we justify their devotion.

Some women have no struggle as to whether they will continue to work outside their home when they marry. No indecision or longing for activity will wrack them. They marry a farmer, a minister, or a country doctor and it becomes a two-way partnership. Who will carry the heavier load? Who will sustain and support the community? I'll bet on the wife every time.

Next year I reach retirement age at my hospital. Many friends have asked if this will mean that I will quit work. Quit work! Not until I quit breathing. I'll work wherever I can; somewhere, I'll always work. Work is medicine, good medicine. I wholeheartedly prescribe it for every woman.

CHAPTER EIGHT

The Four Fears
That Prey on Women

LATE one afternoon a few weeks ago a patient sat on the edge of a chair in my office, gripping her purse tightly and looking everywhere but at my face. "Doctor," she began in a taut voice, "I'm afraid I'm pregnant."

A feeling of the familiarity of the words, the expression on her face, the held-down hysteria in her manner swept over me. I have listened to thousands of women who are afraid—afraid of having a baby, afraid of cancer, afraid of old age, afraid even of menstruation. Sometimes they will admit they are afraid and these are the easiest to help. The women who break a doctor's heart are those who insist gaily that nothing is bothering them, nothing at all, while terror sits in their eyes.

Doctors have known for a long time that fear is a medical problem. It causes, in the beginning, a variety of physical disturbances ranging from an irregularly beating heart to indigestion; some researchers think that over a long period of time the stress of fear can lead to heart trouble and possibly even cancer. In addition to the havoc it causes in the human body, fear strangles personality, murders logic, humor, and the ability to love. A woman swamped by fear functions badly, moving tensely about her home or job and flying into teary rages over spilled cereal or crumpled carbon paper. I've thought a lot about fear and I've come to a conclusion that fear is woman's greatest menace. It can defeat her, mind and body; it is as corrosive as acid and comes in a hundred shapes and sizes.

All human beings suffer from the blight of fear—fear of failure, fear of appearing a fool, fear of high places, fear of darkness. These all are acquired fears; humans are born with only two fears, the fear of a loud noise and the fear of a sudden release of support. In our childhoods we learn the helpful fears, such as fear of fire and fear of falling. We also learn unhelpful fears, such as fear of meeting important people and fear of being unwanted.

Women share all these fears with men, but they have an added problem, fear of their own bodies. Some women are ill at ease with their bodies and those changes which nature causes within them. They distrust and fear the processes of female evolution. This is the fear with which I want to deal.

I thought of this as I examined my new patient and discovered that she would be having her first baby in a little more than six months.

"You said," I remarked casually, "that you are afraid you are pregnant. What's bothering you?"

"I don't know," she answered. Her gaze slid away from mine. "I don't know, I just don't know."

We talked. The woman was young, healthy, happily married. Her home was large enough for the baby and her husband was secure in a good job. "You see," she finished with an embarrassed shrug, "I have no good reason for being upset about this baby. I just feel . . . well . . . trapped."

Trapped is a good word for the feeling a lot of women have during their first pregnancies. I have always compared the situation to that of a soldier who enlists in wartime. He knows he is going to face danger eventually but he buries the knowledge within him and is carefree during training. The dawn inevitably comes when he is loaded into a landing barge and headed for a black beach. He can't turn back now and he doesn't know what lies ahead; he sits there, trapped by circumstances, with his mind swimming in fear.

It's like this with a woman too. She knows from her childhood that she very likely will become a mother. She puts the thought aside and goes ahead through her adolescence, her marriage. Then one day she finds she is pregnant. She can't turn back and she doesn't know what lies ahead. She feels caught, with no control over her destiny. This is the kind of fear that is woman's greatest menace. It has no face, like the fear of making a platform speech or the fear of reception lines. It is a shadow fear, the more dreadful to defeat because it is so senseless. If we hunt a little deeper we will find that the difficulty probably lies in the woman's reluctance to accept the responsibility which this pregnancy will bring. No longer can she be carefree and dependent. She must grow up, share her husband's love, and nurture their child. It isn't only the inevitability of nine months of pregnancy and labor which she cannot side-step, but the endless future.

"Never try to pretend you aren't afraid," I told my patient. "Don't suffer twinges of discomfort in silence just to show how courageous you are. Most important, don't keep this to yourself. Your husband's understanding will be your cure. A woman can face any fear as long as she isn't alone."

I am not a psychiatrist but I've come to realize that usually it is insecure people who have nameless fears. A fear of pregnancy can sometimes be the monster child of the fear of losing a husband. A sensitive man, sharing his wife's concern over the pregnancy and comforting her in the bad moments, can lift the load of fear with his solicitude alone. It is dangerous to fight fear in solitude— no one ever got over a feeling of insecurity by staring out the window at the rain.

Fear of pregnancy comes in many forms, though all

have the same root. Sometimes a woman will say she is afraid of the pain of childbirth. I don't believe this at all. The pain of childbirth isn't sufficient to justify nine months of panic. I know that many women believe that the pain of childbirth is the most severe pain known to mankind, but it isn't. It is a minor pain next to the pain of kidney stones, for example.

One patient told me that she had surveyed her friends who had borne children in an effort to discover how much pain she would have to endure. She got answers that ranged all the way from one woman who told her that there was no pain at all to another who said she would kill herself rather than go through it again. "I'm afraid of pain," this patient told me.

"You're not," I answered emphatically. "You're afraid because you don't know what to expect."

Some women fear their pregnancy because they cannot afford another child. The family has struggled through lean years, sleeping in crowded quarters, living in constant dread of an emergency because they had no savings. Then the mother discovers she is going to have another baby.

"I'm desperate," she tells me. "We simply can't manage another child."

"Nevertheless," I advise her, "your baby is on the way. It is senseless to hate your husband, hate the pregnancy, hate even the unborn child because this happened. Accept it. In this country, at this time, the burden of one extra child isn't insurmountable. If you need help, your church and your community will assist you."

These words are small comfort to a woman in despair. I have something else to tell her that often helps, culled from the knowledge gained in watching babies I have delivered grow to adults. "This child you are now carrying," I say, "may be the greatest comfort of your life—the most beautiful, the sweetest, the most intelligent of all your children. Don't begrudge him life."

When I was younger I used to be mystified at my patients who had gone blithely through three previous pregnancies and then, during their fourth pregnancy, turned into haunted neurotics. My office nurse figured it out and told me.

"They're scared that their luck will run out," she informed me one day when I was puzzling it over.

It's the truth. A mother with three normal, healthy children has a feeling of imminent doom about her fourth child. She figures the law of averages is about to catch up with her and present her with an abnormal baby. Or else she's certain that she won't survive another delivery. She envisions her three children growing up motherless and forlorn. In either case she has a nine-month case of jitters, which is a long time to be apprehensive. Actually a previous medical history of three normal babies and three normal deliveries practically guarantees a fourth normal baby and a fourth normal delivery.

Another woman who suffers acutely from fear during a pregnancy is the one who has had an abnormal baby. She must face the fact that she will be afraid most waking moments and in her nightmares. There is no point in a doctor saying, "Don't worry—chances are that this one will be perfect." She is going to worry anyway until the moment she sees her baby and counts every toe and finger. I advise them to worry out loud, talk it over with their doctors every time their concern becomes acute, discuss it with their husbands every day, if necessary. The martyrs who keep their fears to themselves, gallantly carrying on like someone in a B-movie, scare me to death. As a doctor, I know what deep-buried hysteria is doing to their insides; psychiatrist friends of mine are even more anxious at the possibility of fear damaging their minds.

Women who have an abnormality themselves, such as a birthmark, curvature of the spine, cleft palate, have an equally unsettled pregnancy, full of vivid images of a newborn baby similarly marked. "Talk it out, talk it out," I say. "You're helpless to do anything to change the baby; make sure you don't let fear harm you."

Another massive reason for a woman being afraid to have a baby is, of course, the absence of a legal husband. Every obstetrician has met his or her share of unmarried mothers and faced the spoken or unspoken request that abortion be performed.

"I can't have a baby! I can't!" one career woman shrieked at me. "You've got to do something. This will ruin me!"

"You'll emerge from this a better woman," I said gently.

I truly meant that. Whether she is married or unmarried, the experience of having a baby is something which in itself can be the most wonderful experience of a lifetime. The other side of the coin, giving up a baby for adoption as most unmarried mothers do, is the greatest act of renunciation in the world. A woman's character and personality cannot help but gain from such a searing experience. It's the light to be found in a darkness that seems total.

The first adjustment for an unmarried woman who finds herself pregnant is that she must stop looking for a way out. "You're pregnant," I advise them, "and you're going to stay that way. We will not even discuss whether you are going to have a baby or not, because you are."

Sociologists, theologians, doctors, and philosophers have tramped up and down the subject of the morality and the legality of performing abortions when a woman doesn't want her baby. I'm a practical person, vitally interested ever since I became a doctor in the health and happiness of women, but I can never see any argument for interrupting a pregnancy unless the life of the mother is at stake.

To perform an abortion for any other reason is tampering with fate. This pregnancy may be the only one the woman will have; this unborn child may be a great human being; he may be an unexceptional person who, in a moment of reflex, performs an enormous service to mankind. A doctor isn't prescient; he has no right of eternal judgment.

The last category of pregnant women menaced by fear that occurs to me is the woman who has had a difficult delivery with her first baby. Everyone in her neighborhood has heard a dozen times how many hours she was in labor, how many stitches were taken, and how much blood was transfused. "Never again!" she announces vehemently, adding—to give an illusion of frailty—"My doctor says I shouldn't." When she does become pregnant again, she stages a tantrum in my office. She also gives her husband a heavy time of it, under the biologically unsound assumption that she herself had no part in the conception. All kinds of other resentments toward her husband can be highlighted with this weapon.

In the first place, I've found that women who have a tough time with their first delivery often have a fantastically easy time with their second. I give this information, knowing she won't believe it, and back it with a mention of a possible Caesarean section, which has become a safe operation in these days of antibiotics. It is very seldom needed in these cases.

All women who experience fear over a long period in their pregnancies will suffer symptoms that their sisters rarely know. They will have heartburn, indigestion, constipation, palpitations and, probably, a longer labor. We have no idea of the cause of toxemia of pregnancy, but it occurs so often to unmarried mothers or to women having their first baby that the evidence indicates fear might be the culprit.

In order to fight fear I try to achieve rapport with my

patient. If she tells me everything that is bothering her, we have a chance to get rid of it by counsel.

This brings me to the patients who tell me they adore being pregnant, that they have no unusual symptoms at all to report, that everything is just marvelous. They have symptoms that could be extremely dangerous, like severe headaches, but they don't like to "trouble" me with them. Underneath they are frightened and apprehensive but apparently they have decided that it isn't ladylike to admit such a failing. The women who complain may be irritating, but I infinitely prefer them to the Pollyannas. So does every doctor. Do not confuse my Pollyannas with the majority of pregnant women who truly bloom during their pregnancies into unexpected beauty. These know no fear.

I am reminded, whenever I think of pregnant women hiding their fears, of a patient I had many years ago. She appeared placid and composed whenever I saw her for her checkups; nothing, she insisted, was the least uncomfortable. She worried me dreadfully. "That woman," my nurse once remarked, "is carrying her baby like a sack of groceries." It was a wonderful comparison; the patient was elaborately casual. In her sixth week after her pregnancy, she tried to kill herself. I have tried ever since to penetrate every façade I recognize. It is hard going.

Some fears are passed down lovingly from mother to daughter like family heirlooms. Fear of having a baby is one, providing the mother mentions often enough how agonizing the process is and remembers to pity, aloud, every woman in the neighborhood who becomes pregnant. Her daughter will be terrified during her pregnancy, if she has one. There's a fair chance that she may never want to marry at all.

Painful menstruation is another legacy. I have found that if I am treating a mother for painful menstruation, inevitably I will be treating the daughter as well. The daughter has assumed that all menstruation is painful and she becomes fearful as her turn comes. This tension increases the spasticity of the muscles of the uterus; ergo, the youngster also has painful menstruation. Because of the power of suggestion she may have painful menstruation for the next thirty years. Once a pattern is laid down, it is very difficult to break through. I've noticed, to my sorrow, how many times a pain is perfected by repetition. If you practice enough you can even work up a dandy pattern of headaches. It's just like playing the piano.

We are teaching our children about menstruation and sex much better now than we did in the past, to the relief of the medical profession. Most mothers realize how important it is that young girls accept menstruation as a natural function of the female body. The teen-ager should get a feeling of achievement from the act of menstruation, rather than one of shame and fear.

I'd like to deal next with the fear of cancer, which rides on the backs of some women like a foul monkey. I am flabbergasted at how many women are terrified of cancer. Some women won't even pronounce the word. This leads to enigmatic conversations over the bridge table like:

"Harry has been looking poorly. Do you think he has . . ."

"Could be. Janet, his sister, had it."

"Did she really! I've always wondered but I didn't like to ask."

"Terrible thing."

"Yes, terrible."

The ladies finish their game so sick with fear for their own internal twinges that they won't be able to digest the pineapple and shrimp salad the hostess is going to serve.

This attitude, as I say, really perplexes me. I can think of a dozen afflictions I am really afraid of, and cancer isn't one of them. Cancer in its early stages is usually curable, but some diseases that paralyze the nervous system are not. I would worry far more about these slow cripplers, like muscular dystrophy, and mental illness. These are extremely difficult or impossible to cure, yet I rarely find anyone who is afraid of them.

I've wondered a good deal about the fear of cancer. Are these women afraid of death? I don't really think so. Except for the separation from their families, most people aren't deeply concerned over death. Are they afraid of pain? I doubt it. Most pain is bearable and unbearable pain is difficult to imagine. Are they afraid of the lingering, expensive languishing? Maybe that's it. Too many cancer patients in the past have been nursed at home, pitiful specimens that shocked and frightened the entire family. I suspect that much of the dread of cancer will be lifted when hospitals have room for all cancer patients.

More than all these reasons, though, I believe that fear of cancer is a fear of the unknown. It is a mysterious blackness with a ghoul's name and a sadist's reputation. All too often a person chronically afraid of cancer has just found a convenient label for her chronic fear of insecurity. She is afraid of a future that may find her unloved, unwanted. We could try to remove the fear of cancer with a thorough examination, but we can't cure the fear. She will, if she must, find another label. One woman was pathologically afraid that her appendix would rupture. Someone asked her doctor why he didn't solve the problem by removing her appendix, healthy though it was. "That wouldn't help," he replied gloomily. "Then she'd have to be afraid of cancer. This is easier."

There is, of course, a healthy fear of cancer. Women between the ages of thirty-five and fifty should be aware that cancer is a possibility. They should have annual examinations to ensure that their body functions are in good working order. They should obtain information from their doctors as to which are normal and which are abnormal symptoms. These safeguards tucked under their belts, they should then go about their business without another thought about cancer.

The unhealthy fear of cancer is characterized by a refusal to go to a doctor. The woman is so ridden by the obsession that she has cancer that she cannot bear to have her diagnosis confirmed. This is tragically unreasonable but too common. Consumed with fear, the woman has a strained relation with her husband and children. She veers from tears to a mask of indifference. She can't be interested in her daughter's behavior problem or her husband's triumph—she has her sense of doom to occupy her mind completely.

I have a patient who is justified in her fear of cancer. Her two sisters, her mother and her father died of cancer. She comes to me for reassurance frequently and we discuss it thoroughly. She gets her fears out in the daylight, which is a fair way of dispelling them.

My friends have sometimes asked me what a doctor does when cancer is discovered in a patient. "I suppose," someone once observed, "that you have a case of hysterics on your hands when you tell them."

I have never had such a thing happen. I never say, "I'm afraid you may have cancer. We'll have to investigate." This obviously is both cruel and stupid. Once the diagnosis is made that there is a malignancy, I begin the treatment. Only then, when I have something positive to tell the patient, do I reveal that cancer has been found. Her shock is cushioned by the knowledge that the battle to cure her has already begun.

One patient of mine was twenty-four years old, a beautiful girl with two small children. She was in the hospital for a routine investigation of a minor complaint which was discovered to be cancer. Two mornings after the report had come down, a young nurse making the rounds with me said with terrible concern, "Dr. Hilliard, when are you going to tell that woman she has cancer?"

I started to make a casual answer but I was stopped by her grave expression. "When I am no longer devastated," I answered. "I have to stop resenting that this has happened. When I have recovered my faith in the purpose of life and even death, then I can face her."

The nurse thought it over and nodded understandingly. I was distraught and I knew my fear would be communicated to my patient. She would need my confidence to face what lay ahead of her. When I finally did tell her two days later, she smiled and said, "I know everything will be all right."

The awful thing, as I have tried to stress, is to be alone with a fear. I have never forgotten the patient who thought she had cancer and was too afraid to come to a doctor. Finally, when she was very ill, she was forced to come and see me and I discovered she had advanced cancer, incurable. Her husband and her father insisted that I keep the knowledge from her. I agreed reluctantly, and witnessed the stark terror in her eyes as her doctor and the men she loved kept insisting that nothing serious was the matter with her. She died in the ambulance on the way to the hospital, alone and still frightened.

I will never again accept a case where I am forbidden to tell my patient what is the matter with her. That woman's eyes haunt me. I am sure I could have communicated some strength to her if I could have been honest; I am sure the love of her husband and father, given without a false note, would have comforted her.

One of my dearest friends, another woman doctor, died a few years ago of a nervous ailment that paralyzed her. She had the disease ten years and it was in its final stages; she couldn't move a finger, speak, or turn her head. Suddenly all of us who loved her perceived that she was terrified. Her eyes were wild with fear and it was some time before we could figure out why. Eventually we recalled that a few weeks previously her three closest friends, a minister, another woman doctor, and myself, all had had colds at the same time. To spare her the risk of infection, we had all stopped visiting her and she was left in a sterile vacuum.

Only a few days from death, she needed the warmth of our love to reassure her of the love of God. Without us, she had no faith and she was engulfed by blinding fear for the first time, after years of fearless illness. When we understood this we stayed close by her. Until the moment she died she was never frightened again.

This brings us to the fear of growing old, which again is a fear of not having affection. Women who are facing old age fear desolation; they fear that they have lost their value to their family and consequently they have no value for themselves. They face loneliness and having to be dependent.

Women whose sole sustaining asset has been their appearance are the most pathetic of all. Through their thirties and forties they have put so much emphasis on attractiveness of looks and manner that they have given no affection, help, or interest. Naturally they cannot expect to receive any affection, help, or interest. As their faces and figures deteriorate with age, they panic. We all know wretched old women with orange hair, round spots of rouge, and a determinedly girlish cackle. They are the saddest spectacles of the human race. I know them as a doctor because they are ravaged inside with the symptoms of fear—tremors, bowel and bladder irregularity, dyspepsia, insomnia.

Working women, as they become older, are exhausted by their fear of losing their jobs to a younger woman. They dread poor health, which they can't afford. Housewives, as they age, fear the dissolution of their homes and the end of their usefulness. They are frightened that their children will become indifferent to them, that they will become an odious burden instead of the adored comfort they used to be.

It is a sickening truth: old people fear living far more than they do dying.

These fears reflect a negative attitude toward old age; there is a positive one. A woman past fifty has more to offer her employer and her community than she ever has known. She is serene, experienced, sound in her judgment, and tolerant. If she avoids the paralyzing twins, fear and self-pity, she can be a beneficent influence in charitable work, in local government such as school boards and rate-payers associations, in improving her community visually through garden clubs or culturally through a symphony-orchestra association. Her local church needs her wise hands for baking and sewing projects to help unfortunates. Her family, if she can abide their theories on child raising, will rejoice in her help as a baby sitter. And the world can always find a welcome for a cake baked the old-fashioned way, instead of with a box of powder and a cup of water.

As for appearance, beauty and grace improve with age —as any artist will tell you. Television producers have found that young faces appear shallow and uninteresting; older faces, wrinkled and caressed by time, are fascinating. Age, worn with dignity and charm, is a delight. A woman with no fears to irritate and tighten her nerves is a valued addition to any gathering.

I don't mean to give the impression that fear can be conquered at one gulp, forever. It never can. Everyone who is sensitive to life is afraid. The danger in fear is that it can make itself at home in our minds and sit there, breeding nightmares, doubts, terror, pain and suspicion. It must be met whenever it occurs and beaten, if only for the moment.

There are two reactions to fear: a woman can be a stoic and endure it, or she can have faith in herself, faith in the future, faith in the love of those she loves. In the process of stoicism, everything dies. In faith, everything is bright and moving.

Never face a fear alone. You need people who can give you love and affection and these can never be abstract. To know you are loved, you have to have the touch of a hand.

Since fear is unreasonable, never try to reason with it. So-called "positive thinking" is no weapon against fear. Only positive faith can rout the black menace of fear and give life a radiance.

My faith is simple, but means everything to me: I believe that man was born to love and be loved and moreover is loved. I know, from watching moments of tragedy, defeat, and despair change and grow into beauty and happiness, that if you truly love, "all things will work together for good." But if you demand security and happiness as your right and are wary of loving, fear will infiltrate the whole structure and everything is lost.

"Though I walk through the valley of the shadow . . . I will fear no evil, for thy rod and thy staff they comfort me. . . ."

CHAPTER NINE

Woman's Greatest Enemy Is Fatigue

I HADN'T been in practice very long when a colleague asked me how I was enjoying my profession. I considered the question carefully.

"You know," I answered, "I believe I get more pleasure out of making well women happy than in curing a definite disease."

"Ah," nodded my friend knowingly, "the fatigue cases."

Fatigue is such a common problem that there are few doctors who don't encounter it in one of its various forms every day. In dealing with women, which is my province, we use the word fatigue to define several dozen states of mind and body: the childless housewife who says she is tired all the time; the middle-aged woman who has headaches; the businesswoman who wakes up every morning more tired than when she went to bed; the young mother whose back aches. Fatigue inexorably accompanies the great changes within a woman —the girl reaching adolescence, the pregnant woman, the woman in her menopause.

Fatigue is the word for the intangible that means the difference between a woman who walks with a spring in her step and a woman who wishes she were dead. It is a word that is being used in medical research, along with "stress," to explain the basic cause of heart attacks and ulcers in young, ambitious people. Stress and fatigue are modern calamities, the result of the run-run-run environment of our hurrying civilization. They go together because fatigue is the result of stress, when too much strain has been put on the mental and emotional side of a person, causing a possible breakdown of the physical.

I believe fatigue to be the greatest enemy a woman ever faces and, tragically enough, the one she is least likely to recognize. Fatigue, carried to its extreme, can shorten her life or lead to mental illness. It will sap her strength and leave her at the mercy of transient infections. It can break up her marriage by turning her into a shrew, and blight the lives of her children; by keeping the safety catch off the trigger of her temper it can lose her her best friends. Most terrible of all, it robs her of the joy and vitality without which any life is gray and meaningless.

I must explain what I mean by fatigue. I don't mean

103

the physical exhaustion of a woman who has been doing the spring cleaning for a week, or nursing an invalid over several sleepless nights and days, or working overtime on an inventory or a giant, supercolossal sale. Those women are merely tired, a state of enormous weariness which can be cured by one good night's sleep. When I speak of fatigue I'm speaking of the sensation of being tired which continues for months and years—a state of apathy toward tomorrow, of headaches, backaches, crying spells, heaviness of body and mind. I often describe it as a lack of tone which shows in the sag of her body when she walks and the dullness in her voice when she talks.

I see hundreds of women suffering from fatigue every year. Now that we have a word for the condition, many doctors have taken the trouble to keep medical records on the subject. They find that four out of every five patients who come to them with fatigue symptoms only, have nothing whatever the matter with them physically. The fifth may have anemia, high blood pressure, an underactive thyroid or a low-grade infection. All these conditions can be treated within the framework of our medical education. To cure fatigue a doctor must also be a sociologist, a psychiatrist, an efficiency expert and a Solomon. This is the part of my practice which I find most challenging and most rewarding.

Every woman will experience fatigue several times in her lifetime and it seems a pity to me that adolescents aren't warned about it in the routine way that they are informed of the other enemy of the body, physical illness. A woman first experiences fatigue during the period of from twelve to seventeen years of age when endocrinal changes take place within her. The symptoms come on gradually, almost imperceptibly, and depart the same way, but every woman can recall that as a teenager she was almost impossible to waken in the morning and felt heavy-eyed through the day. During this important growing period parents should insist that their daughters get sufficient rest—and I appreciate what a difficult thing I'm asking. Three or four nights a week should be set apart as early-to-bed nights and let the wails and protests fall on deaf ears. A young girl's system must be protected against the demands of her social life.

The next endocrinal change within a woman takes place during pregnancy, which is always accompanied by fatigue. Obstetricians invariably say to prospective mothers, "Now eat plenty of meat, fruit and vegetables and be sure to get sufficient rest." The patient nods in perfect agreement—I've seen them—and makes a mental calculation that what the doctor really means is to continue her routine exactly as it was, adding an orange here and a calcium pill there. When she is about seven months pregnant she will find herself crying fretfully over carrots that have boiled dry. Fatigue is beating her down, and when I meet her in the delivery room I will find a nervous, overwrought woman who will be in no condition in a few days to care for an infant.

By the term "sufficient rest" during pregnancy, we doctors mean an hour or two *in bed* after lunch. Give the rest priority over phone calls, neighbors dropping in, and the urge to dust the coffee table. It is more than the whim of a doctor, it's an absolute necessity if the prospective mother is to survive her confinement with her cheery personality intact.

This is perfectly manageable for the woman having her first child—a note on the door, the telephone receiver off the hook, and a humorous but dead-earnest warning to the neighbors will take care of all interruptions. I realize that the mother who already has a child or two in her home is in a different position. Sometimes when I am telling such a mother to get an afternoon nap she looks at me over the head of the squirming three-year-old in her lap and her expression goes blank. I know she is trying to decide whether to laugh or brain me with my medical dictionary.

Nevertheless, it is possible for mothers of small children to get sufficient rest during their pregnancies. Usually it can be managed if the mother goes to bed as soon as her child has his nap; sometimes it can be done by putting the child firmly in a play pen or behind the gate across the door of his bedroom. The child will be rewarded with the attention of a mother who is rested and relaxed.

The first three months after the new baby is born are probably the days of the greatest fatigue a woman ever knows. Her body is changing back to its cycle, which alone can cause fatigue, and her small baby is hungry at midnight and five in the morning and assorted hours in between. Frequently the spent mother falls asleep while nursing her infant, waking with a start an hour later to find the unburped baby crying with gas pains. It's hard to recommend any solution to this problem, short of the expensive one of hiring help. The situation can be kept within the bounds of human endurance if the infant's father helps with meals and dishes and a night feeding; fortunately for my patients, very few husbands are shortsighted enough to insist on service as usual during the three-month ordeal.

The last endocrinal change a woman experiences is during her menopause, which generally occurs between the ages of forty-five to forty-eight, though it varies from woman to woman. The menopause is always accompanied by exhaustion because of the physical glandular changes taking place within the woman. These physical changes combine with the strange, lonely feeling of futility a woman gets during this period of her life. Rest once more becomes as important as it was during her pregnancies and when she was a teen-ager. Along with rest she needs compensation for that this-is-the-end-of-the-world sensation, some engrossing hobby, something new to reaffirm the reality of a busy happy future.

All these are the unavoidable fatigues, the times in every woman's life when she actively must plan to keep herself normal. If she is unaware of what is happening to her, as many women are, she will sink into depression and moodily wonder if her health is breaking down, if her boss is planning to fire her, if her husband is being unfaithful, if her children are turning against her. If she had given herself sufficient rest, she would have been spared much of this churning misery.

I get another type of fatigue case very frequently in my office. The woman is in her twenties and is physically in perfect condition. She has two small children, under school age, and she complains of a backache.

"Of course your back aches," I tell her briskly; sympathy is not going to be particularly helpful. "You have two preschool children and you're tired out. You can expect to be tired, all the time, until they are in school."

I have given up looking for a solution for this problem: There isn't one. A woman who has a baby has to face up to the realization that she will be tired for the next five years. The preschool child needs constant attention twenty-four hours a day for five years. She must supervise his meals, train him to go to the bathroom, dress himself, protect himself from automobiles and rainstorms, teach him the English language and social deportment, nurse him when he is sick, and comfort him through his nightmares. Certainly she is tired.

The next step, after a new mother has accepted her fate, is to minimize the damage that such prolonged weariness might do to her relations with her friends, her ability to raise her child in a warm friendly environment, and her marriage. The most important relationship to be preserved is the last one. If the mother has nothing to offer her husband returning home in the evening but the chaos of mismanaged children and herself near tears, she had better plan immediately for the evenings she will soon be spending without him.

Every wife has a positive moral obligation to have something of herself left over from her home and children for her husband. The first essential of her marriage is that she be happy and relaxed when he is home, that there be no turmoil which he must smooth over. A wife who is tired is incredibly unreasonable, and while her humor and understanding are at their lowest ebb she is most likely to find herself in a screaming, hysterical tirade against her husband. A few of these can rock any marriage.

I must deal at this time with the problem of sex as related to fatigue. Women suffering from fatigue almost invariably lose their interest in sexual relations. They withhold themselves from their husbands, I sometimes suspect, partly out of spite. Because they are unhappy and exhausted, they want to inflict misery on someone else and this is the first and best weapon at hand. It is also the weapon that hurts the most and it is the one no woman should ever use. It is a sin against the spirit.

A woman bent on avoiding sexual relations with her husband goes through a classic charade in order to succeed. She begins early in the evening to warn him with unlovely subtlety against any advance, moaning that she is tired beyond all feeling, sighing when it is necessary for her to rise and turn off the radio, falling on the bed limply and with marvelously ingenious yawns. He gets the idea. They bid one another good night politely.

The energy she has just been expending in this performance is far greater than the energy she would require to meet the simple demands of a normal married life. Her sense of guilt is smothered hastily in a thoroughly unjustified conviction that a sex life shouldn't be demanded of her—poor, overworked woman that she

108

is. The frustrations and anguish of planning endless excuses are vastly more tiring than a full sex life would ever be.

I frankly advise any woman in the grip of such a silent struggle to relax and put her Thespian skill to work at convincing her husband he is desired. She will be rewarded by the release of the tension that has ruined her evenings and by the flowering of her marriage. By nourishing her husband's ego, she ensures his contentment which, in turn, will ensure her own.

Next, she must get at the base of the problem: her fatigue. I think the mother of preschool children needs to work out a job analysis, just as industrial workers do. She must list all the essentials of her home management and space them out so that two heavy jobs don't fall on the same day. Then, when she is working out a schedule, she must put "Rest for Mother" on the list among the essentials. She needs time in the day for herself and I usually recommend to my tired young mothers that they set aside ten-thirty in the morning for a half hour of sitting with their feet up, sipping at some kind of nourishment like orange juice or milk. She can sit in the back yard during the summer where she can supervise her children or by a window giving a view of them in the winter. Unless a catastrophe befalls them, such as a skinned knee, she should refrain from the temptation of leaping to her feet at their slightest whimper. In the afternoon she must lie down. I know it will be a major piece of engineering to carve an hour or so out of every day, but being well rested is as vital to her happiness as breathing is to her life.

I have one patient who told me she thinks she could never have survived the years when her children were babies if she hadn't found a sitter in the neighborhood who was willing to come in every afternoon from three-thirty to four o'clock. "There's a Honey Dew near our house," this patient told me. "I used to go there and drink coffee and read *The New Yorker* for a half hour. It calmed me down and kept me going."

I don't know how many times this young-family fatigue is complicated and intensified to a frenzy by a husband who is unappreciative. A vital aspect of marriage, as I said before, is the nourishing of one another's egos, and a husband who fails to praise his wife's cooking, or the way the house sparkles, or the adroit way she answered a four-year-old's query about the origin of babies is inflicting a deep wound. A woman can mull over a series of indifferent moments until her nerves are raw, going from fury to despondency in the squirrel cage of her mind. Her fatigue is bound to increase and she is certain to wind up in some doctor's office and ask if there isn't something seriously wrong—she's too tired even to climb stairs.

It's surprising how quickly a doctor can reach the real source of the trouble. He first takes her medical history and her present symptoms, then he finds how much housework she does, what organizations she belongs to, what she does with her evenings. When his careful medical examination has revealed no physical cause for the fatigue, he is ready to prescribe. My favorite prescription for an apathetic marriage is a meal in a restaurant. Mealtimes at home with a young family can rarely be described as delightful; the parents have no time for conversation because they are too busy policing the manners and intake of their offspring.

"You've got to regain that zest you and your husband had for each other before the children came," I tell my patients. "If you can afford it, arrange to meet him downtown once a week for dinner. If you can't, then at least go out for a sandwich and a cup of coffee every now and then." It's a therapy that balances weeks of scrambled, clamorous meals with the children. Once his wife is in focus again as a woman, it generally follows that his treatment of her becomes more thoughtful.

110

Once the children are all in school, mothers generally feel as frisky as colts. They spend hours wandering through department stores, attending fashion shows, bazaars, bridge afternoons, luncheons and quilting bees. Late in the afternoon they hurtle home, slam some pots and pans on the stove, deal with an avalanche of leggy youngsters and end up with as big a case of fatigue as when the children were small.

A woman continually must arrange her life to give herself time to relax. If her children are in school then she must realize that her work period is concentrated at the end of the day; somewhere in the early afternoon she has to find time to rest with her feet up.

A businesswoman needs the same sort of organizing but she has a greater problem. If she is maintaining a home at the same time she has three choices: (a) To do her job properly and let her home go; (b) To let the job go and keep her home in perfect order or (c) Fatigue. The difficulty is that an astonishing number of otherwise intelligent women choose fatigue rather than have their homes less than spotless and their jobs a notch under perfection. When they have been suffering from fatigue long enough they will fail at both jobs, but it is hard to convince most women of this until after their breakdowns.

I heartily object to women who work a five-day week and then spend Saturday and Sunday doing a week's house cleaning. They are headed for trouble and in the meantime they collect no medals. Personally I would award them a spangled dunce cap. Their weekend should be saved for rest and recreation; during the five-day work week they can spread their housework out in humane doses in the evenings.

Most business girls who come to me with fatigue expect me to tell them they are working too hard. Hard work rarely causes fatigue in the sense that I mean it. Their fatigue is the result of two factors: lack of appreciation, and monotony. Without a smattering of respect for her efforts, the business girl is a maze of frustrations which will bring on fatigue. If her boss is such an unkind clod that he fails to thank her occasionally for her efforts, I suggest that the girl search for warmth elsewhere—in a bowling league, an art class or in hammering pewter bracelets.

Monotony is also a breeding ground for fatigue. An artist can work fourteen hours over a canvas and feel exhilarated when he is finished; a business girl working on ledgers or ironing shirts is worn out in two hours. The coffee break was designed to relieve this type of fatigue. I also recommend that the business girl go home to some interest after her work. Some women offset the monotony of their working lives by furnishing a room or a small apartment with colors they love, records, or books or pictures that will comfort them. Often the process of furnishing such a retreat will be, in itself, beneficial.

I must warn single business girls of a period of enormous emotional turmoil which awaits them in their late thirties and early forties when they first realize that they will never marry. This is a dreadful time for a woman to survive, days of bitterness and fear for her future, and nights of loneliness and tears. The resultant fatigue from such a struggle is prostrating. Such women are so weary that they are confounded when I advise them to take on more interests, more clubs and other recreations. Once her battered soul is past this upheaval, and her menopause is over, she can look forward to a marvelous life. With no children or husband on her mind, she is really sailing in her fifties. The fifty-year-old single women could run the world if the world would give them a chance.

Sometimes when I am questioning a fatigue sufferer about her home environment I discover that she has her parents or her husband's parents living with her. I put this down as a primary cause of fatigue, not because the older people cause an excessive amount of work but because of the confusion and controversy which always seem to accompany such an arrangement. The woman gnaws on the same bone of petty grievances all day long, stifling the desire to say something or throw something. The mental conflict naturally brings her to a state of fatigue.

First I recommend that my patient stop scurrying around in her mind looking for exits. She must accept the fact that the situation is never going to change; she must change. This acceptance alone relaxes the tension. Next the woman must arrange with tact if possible— and without it if necessary—that she and her husband have some time to themselves every day when they have privacy. Sometimes it can be solved by separate dinner hours for the older people.

Many types of fatigue are beyond any doctor's power to solve. I find that women suffering from the fatigue of monotony present the most difficult problem. Frequently they are women who have raised a large family who are now grown; there is nothing left to do. Occasionally they are wealthy women whose husbands have provided them with maids to keep their homes clean, private schools to supervise their children, and cooks to provide their meals. With nothing to fill their lives but leisure, they are nearly ill with fatigue.

These people need something to do, and I believe a community activity is the best solution, something that will keep them in a hubbub of people. Many times, though, I have been unable to help and I have had gently to pass them on to a psychiatrist.

There is another type of fatigue I might mention here which is beyond the help of most medical doctors— the spiritual fatigue that results from selfishness. Self-centered people, involved in a ceaseless, grinding necessity to be impressive, suffer from fatigue. They must stop grasping and plotting in order to become rested, about as tall an order as getting a neurotic to stop worrying. Generally only a psychiatrist can get at the root of the problem. Selfish people also invent more fatigue in order to keep attention focused on their own frailties, to shift the household duties on their husbands, and keep their children in line. The assumed weariness then becomes the only consistent form of discipline in the home: "Don't get dirty—Mommy works so hard to keep you clean" and "Don't argue—Mommy is so tired." Mommy needs some psychiatric help and so will her children if she keeps on feeding their guilt complexes.

I wish I had kept records of the number of times I have found that the solution for fatigue is part-time work. Housewives who are lonely and frustrated by the repetitive tasks of cleaning a home; women in the grip of the menopause who are frightened and upset; women living with older people who rasp on their nerves—all can be helped by getting out into another world.

As you can see, some fatigue is caused by too much to do and some by too little; some is a by-product of a glandular change and some is the result of monotony or pure selfishness. Fatigue is such a common occurrence that it has been called the Great North American Disease. It follows every bitter emotion known to the human race—pain, loneliness, bitterness, boredom, fear, jealousy and indecision—and prolongs them all by making its victim too tired to cure herself. It is our greatest squirrel cage, and the greatest danger to her happiness a woman will ever meet. But it's part of our lives; let's treat fatigue with good sense—and beat it.

CHAPTER TEN

Women's Greatest Blessing

NEARLY every day that I am in my office, some middle-aged woman leans across my desk as shamed and fearful as though she had just garroted her mother and whispers: "Doctor, I think I'm in the change."

"The change!" I whoop with real delight. "Well, you're in for an interesting time. I can promise you that the best years of your life are ahead of you."

"Ahead of me!" says my patient, looking around wildly for a butterfly net. "Surely you mean behind me."

"Ahead of you," I repeat firmly. "Do you know what I call the menopause? It's women's greatest blessing."

I've got another half hour of fast talking to do before my patient can begin to be convinced, but she's going to have a hard time disputing my arguments.

There has never been enough written about the menopause. The modern woman, the same girl who can tell you when the second-year molars are formed in a fetus or the psychiatric term for submerged memory, this enlightened woman has surrounded the inevitable process of menopause with doom and gloom. She expects it will whiten her hair, make her pregnant, and bring on insanity. She nervously refers to it by a phrase drummed up in some voodoo séance—"the change."

It has often struck me, as I try to calm such a woman who is confused by superstition and untruths, that many of the hazards of the menopause would be cut to a minimum if every woman was well equipped with information about what to expect and how to protect herself. Once a woman accepts the fact that the menopause is a sometimes uncomfortable, but frequently comical, beginning of a better life, she can shrivel the terror and despondency that seem to be associated with the word.

To begin with, the menopause is an unavoidable process of the human female body. It is the counterpart to adolescence, which introduces a woman to the cyclic life of menstruation and fertility, and it is so similar to adolescence that I invariably compare the two.

The adolescent is a miserable, exasperating, oversensitive, complex personality; she is prone to deep exhaustion and bursts of energy; she finds herself weeping forlornly because no one understands her and jumping with glee over a phone call; she is fussy to a fault about her appearance; she can be a vixen, from no apparent cause; when she is lonely, which happens often, she eats; her menstrual periods are unpredictable.

Throw in a few hot flushes and you have the menopause.

I don't mean to minimize out of proportion what is at best a peculiar and disorganized feminine transition. The menopause is accompanied by some of the most infuriating symptoms a woman can possibly experience. It can rob her of her memory, so that she stops in the midst of introducing her best friends because she has forgotten both their names. It fools her by pulling a trap door out from under her normal energy and dropping her into a pit of lassitude on the day she had planned to paint the bathroom. It causes her face to flush a heroic red at a moment when she needs every scrap of poise she possesses; instead, she is blinded by the perspiration running through her mascara. The menopause can cause unexpected hemorrhages during a public event and scar a woman with shame she'll

116

never forget. It can cause such an upheaval of personality that a serene and competent woman office manager will turn and scream at a younger woman. It can even delude a normally composed woman into believing that she is losing her mind, her husband, and her children.

Most mysterious of all, every one of these symptoms can disappear overnight and not return again for a week, a month, maybe a year, maybe never. I sometimes call the menopause "the Thing." It changes its shape and personality constantly. One day I'm treating a woman who is bleeding profusely and the next day she has stopped bleeding; one day she is irritable and discouraged and the next she is planning a picnic with her grandchildren. During the menopause a woman can have either heavier periods of menstruation which can occur quite close together, or she can have sparse, scanty periods months apart. She can also, within a year, have both varieties. The menopause is officially over only when there has been no menstruation for a year. Even after this interval a normal period, with the attending symptoms of bloating, backache and breast changes, may appear. Although this isolated period is probably normal, any irregular bleeding after the menopause should be reported to your doctor, just as any irregular bleeding between your periods should be. Your doctor has a responsibility to you—and you to him. Keep an accurate record of your irregular periods; this is no time for vagueness. Never panic about malignancy because of the bizarre behavior of your interior. Let your doctor reassure you. Any severe loss of energy should also be reported immediately, especially in the case of a working woman. A certain amount of fatigue is natural, but excess weariness may be due to anemia, resulting from the heavy loss of blood that lowers hemoglobin content.

Another of its enigmas is that no gynecologist, psychiatrist, or endocrinologist can predict in any individual when the menopause will start or how long it will last. In this respect the menopause again compares with its younger sister, adolescence. Sometimes a child of eleven is ravaged by all the miseries of adolescence; another girl will shag flies with the boys on the corner lot until she is sixteen, joyfully unaware of any torment. Some girls suffer terribly in their teens; others just seem to grow taller and rounder without a pang.

This is the way it is with the menopause. I have had a patient who started her menopause at thirty-nine and another who ended hers when she was fifty-nine. Both of these cases are extremely rare. The average menopause begins at forty-five, reaches its peak as a nuisance at forty-seven, and is gone at fifty. I've known women who were truly tortured by their menopause and I've known others who had no discernible menopause at all.

In almost every country of the world a new area of research is being explored—womanhood's menopause. It is a tough and unrewarding chore. It is still impossible to make a test that will establish that a woman is either in or out of her menopause; all diagnoses are made by deduction. Controlled experiments are nearly hopeless because laboratory experimental animals that have a menopause, like the rabbit, do not pass through any demonstrable change. Most of the experiments, therefore, are aimed at finding some method of maintaining a better hormone balance during the menopause in order to reduce some of the distressing symptoms. The experiments began only a few years ago. Until recently a woman's life expectancy wasn't much beyond the menopause years; now she lives twenty years more.

We do have some information. Owing to some unknown reason, the ovaries eventually become unresponsive and the menstrual cycle slows until the ovaries and accessory sex organs deteriorate to the point where they cannot function at all and menstruation ceases. During this period hormones and certain glands behave eccentrically and there is a corresponding emotional up-heaval.

Women who have had hysterectomies are special and fascinating cases. If both ovaries are removed, the menopause begins immediately, of course, and the symptoms are exaggerated by the added stress and shock of the operation. If the ovaries are left *in situ*, as is done whenever possible with younger women, the patient recovers from the operation in six or eight weeks and enters into a period of wonderful health. When she reaches her time of menopause, she begins to have the flushes, fatigue and anxiety common to the Thing. Since she isn't menstruating, and therefore misses the positive symptom of irregular bleeding, she may be mystified. But it's the same menopause, all right, with almost the same nuisance value. Every woman has her own pattern—the only constant fact is its infinite variety.

Generations of panicky women have spawned enough untruths about the menopause to panic the next five generations.

For example, it is said that a woman's hair turns white during her menopause. This isn't true; the graying or whitening of hair is a process not connected with the menopause.

It is also said that the menopause causes women to become insane. The menopause cannot, in itself, cause insanity. An underlying mental illness may become more apparent during the menopause; investigating psychiatrists always can find a clearly recognizable pattern of behavior before the menopause that should have been cause for concern. Periods of depression are a common experience for many women and these often become overemphasized by the woman's concern over being depressed. Emotional tone can be as inconstant as nervous or physical energy and should not be classified as a separate condition.

Many women believe they are more fertile during the

menopause, and thousands of innocent rabbits are subjected to pregnancy tests as a result. This is obviously illogical, since the reproductive organs are drying up. Occasionally a woman does have a baby during her menopause; I suspect that the sensation this causes among her friends magnifies what is a minor statistic into a major phenomenon. Women are less fertile during their menopause than they have been since they were sixteen.

Another of the pitfalls of the menopause that many women fear is addiction. Statistics do indicate that a high proportion of women drug addicts and alcoholics are of the menopause age. These disasters are part of the same pattern as mental illness; they cannot befall a personality that didn't already have a deep neurotic tendency before the menopause began. The women who become mentally ill, alcoholics, or drug addicts are the tragedies of an entire civilization; the menopause alone cannot cause such a breakdown. Doctors are on the alert for this hazard, even to avoiding encouraging too much dependence on the use of hormones.

Last summer I attended a conference of two hundred women doctors, members of the International Federation of Medical Women, which was held in Rome. We discussed the menopause at some length and I was fascinated to learn that women the world over share the same indignities of body and spirit during the menopause.

I was amused to discover, however, that the emphasis on these indignities varied from country to country. The Scandinavian women doctors, who practice in countries noted for their energetic and industrious women, were preoccupied chiefly with the loss of efficiency of women in menopause. This is one of the rumors about the menopause that is absolutely true.

French women doctors, on the other hand, showed a fine Gallic disdain for the problem of loss of efficiency.

Their patients, they reported, were wild with anxiety that their love lives were over. This is another truth about the menopause: It does result in a temporary loss of sexual desire.

I'll begin with the latter problem, because it is handiest and not because the majority of women in this country share the French women's concern. I suspect that nearly half the women in this country don't care much for sex at all.

It is a normal reaction at the onset of the menopause that a woman's sexual appetite begins to wane; subsequently the appetite becomes completely capricious for the duration of the menopause. It isn't too unreasonable that many women in their mid-forties then assume, mistakenly, that the physical side of their marriage is ended forever and a more platonic relationship will take its place. This sets up as nasty a Freudian problem as any soap opera can offer.

The husband has two alternatives: he can become a celibate, an unnatural arrangement that over a period of years actually can cause him to become impotent; or he can seek a younger woman, as thousands of middle-aged men do. In the latter case he will add a crushing blow to his wife's sense of security, which is already tottering.

Also, the woman in menopause runs the risk of being suspicious and fearful over nothing—thus building her own tragedy. Her husband is bound to be working harder, building toward his retirement, and his late nights probably are spent in his office, working.

If the husband remains faithful, running the real risk of permanent impotency, the marriage has a further peril. His wife, when she has finished her menopause, will be a renewed woman, full of zest and excitement and ready to enjoy a full marriage again.

The solution of this dilemma is up to the woman. During her menopause she must make sure that she maintains sexual relations with her husband, despite her weakened inclination. It's like keeping up the payments on her home—in this case she is ensuring that her sound and healthy marriage will last.

The working woman can be battered to helpless tears by the menopause unless she is prepared to accept certain truths. Much of my practice is with business and professional women and I have formed some opinions, over the years, that can be helpful.

The most important is that a woman's energy is cut to two thirds of her normal complement during her menopause. By this time in their careers many women are at the peak in their fields; they are supervisors, department managers, principals, lawyers, and doctors with large practices, editors, owners of small businesses. It is a time when they can least afford to lose any efficiency.

Nonetheless it has happened, and these working women must first accept that they cannot fight nature and survive. They must adjust, for the few years of their menopause, to a less demanding schedule. In my case I gave up my office hours on Fridays; I spent the afternoon having my hair done and in recreations like golf and fishing. Another woman, who cannot give herself a day off, would have to avoid all overtime, all extra assignments, all deadlines. This is the hardest lesson to learn. Many women feel challenged by their menopause; they attempt to prove that their body may be getting older, but they themselves are younger than ever, raring to go. In a battle between an exhausted body and a game spirit, the body wins every time.

Another bitter lesson for the well-organized businesswoman, whose filing-case memory has never failed, is that both her memory and her ability to organize will desert her entirely for a day or two at a time. She can't remember the price of a line of stockings she has been selling for twenty years. Her boss wants to know if Smithers picked up his order; she's going to have to devise some cunning way of remembering who Smithers is.

These are the bad days. One woman, having a bad day early in her menopause, drove through downtown Toronto, stopping meticulously at every green light and driving through every red one. On one of my bad days I was addressing some student nurses and couldn't think of the word "induction," a word an obstetrician uses as often as a cook uses butter. On such days I would greet a favorite patient I had known for years and discover that I had forgotten her name. I'd check her chart before I could say "Hello, Mary."

A day like that, if it isn't expected, can give any woman the hysterical impression that she is losing her mind. Here's where her sense of humor is vital. On the mornings when she wakens feeling edgy and listless, when deciding what to wear appears an overwhelming problem, she knows she is due for a bad day. One woman used to warn her family, "This is going to be a grumpy day—batten the hatches!"; another, a saleswoman, blithely advised the other clerks, "Don't expect me to add two and two today and if Mrs. Van Tyler comes in, I've left for Mexico."

The bad days are invested with a special sense of adventure. They are the days to write down everything you do or plan to do, to postpone conferences, shopping trips, house cleaning, and discussions of politics. It might also be a good time to eat out; one woman, on her bad days, twice neglected to cook any meat for dinner.

In a prominent position among the peculiarities put hot flushes. The back of the hand wiping a sweaty forehead is the coat of arms of the menopause. The flush begins with a warming of the body which gives a cosy sensation and heightened color to the face. This is dandy if it stops there, but it usually doesn't. A medium flush turns the face a lobster red and an all-out perspiration

123

flush gives the impression that the victim has been shoveling coal in the hold for the past hour.

I used to make a little bet with myself, for moderate stakes, when a flush began. I named the medium one "straight flush," and the other "royal flush." I wish I could have done as well at poker.

Another oddity of the menopause is that energy can vanish overnight and leave a woman as helpless as if she were ill. One patient of mine had invited six guests for dinner during a buoyant moment. She wakened the day of the party feeling like a jellyfish. She not only couldn't remember whom she had invited, she couldn't decide what to serve. She struggled weakly with the complexities of a menu, made out a shopping list, and dragged herself to the grocery store. She then discovered she'd forgotten the list. She found it, months later, neatly filed with her recipe for goulash.

The menopause seems to strike hardest the efficient woman who has spent her life doing her housework or her job with an unshakable system. When her schedules break down, as break down they must if she tries to bull through them like a thirty-year-old, she becomes frantic. The sweetly vague housewife, on the other hand, the one who never served dinner on time in her life, sails through her menopause just a little more vague than usual.

The emotional reaction to the menopause depends on two factors: hormone balance and stress. A woman undergoing no strain in her business, social, or family life and with consistent hormone balance would suffer no effects at all, but she is a rare bird. Most women find they have little control over the depth of their emotions. They hate and love more fiercely, feel jealousy and loneliness more intensely.

All human beings need affection, or else living is meaningless. The woman in menopause needs it most of all and the tragedy is that she often deprives herself of it because she stops giving affection. What I mean is this:

A patient came to me and said she had been crying for hours because her husband had stopped kissing her good-by in the mornings. She described how she sat at the breakfast table, drooping with misery, while he airily waved at her and went off to work. "For twenty years I've been going to the door and kissing him good-by," she wailed. "Now look how he treats me!"

"It's your own fault," I told her. "If you want to be kissed in the morning, you'd better go to the door with him. You can't expect him to change the habits of twenty years."

Another woman was upset because her teen-age daughter didn't help her with the housework. As it happened, this mother had never wanted or needed her daughter's help in the past. "You can't expect her to be clairvoyant," I commented. "How is she supposed to know that you are measuring her love by the amount of dishes she washes? You get busy and give her some affection."

A middle-aged woman can be awfully dreary. Her personality is colored by imagined woe and self-pity. Even her clothes are chosen without enthusiasm or inspiration. One fashion writer refers to a certain aimless shade of blue as "menopause blue." It's an insipid color.

I've noticed that the hardest person in the world to love is an adolescent; the next hardest is a woman in her menopause. Now everyone laughs at and understands the adolescent. I wish they would do the same for the menopauser. Hiding the menopause under a heavy cloak of shame has been our undoing—menopause is not a synonym for senility.

Families can help a woman in her menopause best by not sympathizing with her, but they should at the same time reduce the strain and everyday irritations in the household. The greatest gift the mother can get is a

125

peaceful, cheerful dinner hour. Father makes a point of bringing home his best story and doesn't leave all his charm and good humor at his work.

Don't listen to her troubles—she'll never get stopped telling you about them. You don't console an adolescent who is crying because she can't find her yellow scarf; you tell her to pull herself together and go out and play tennis. You say it gently and you smile.

This is precisely the philosophy for the menopause. Recreation is as vital a tonic as anything a doctor can prescribe. Women in their menopause are thickening around their middles—a condition brought about chiefly from overeating during their depressed periods—and I could never see the point of rubbing in expensive creams to make the face look like thirty-five while allowing the body to get lumpy and saggy like a sixty-five-year-old's. Recreation should include something athletic enough to keep the middle of the body supple. In addition, hitting a long shot off the tee is not conducive to thoughts that life is not worth living.

I might include laughter as a major part of therapy. A light magazine article, a silly technicolor movie, a buffoon on a television show—one good dose of laughter should be taken daily.

Now, with all these multiple problems before them, why do I tell my patients to be glad their menopause has started? Why do I call it women's greatest blessing? I'll tell you.

In the first place, the cycle of menstruation imposes a greater burden on women's emotions than they can ever realize until the cyclic life is over. Every doctor is familiar with the cliché of the married woman between the ages of thirty and forty-five: "Doctor, I only have one good week a month!" The week after her period she could lick wildcats; two weeks later she begins to sink; three weeks later she is gloomy; she hits rock bottom the day before her period begins. Twelve times a year, for thirty years, this pattern is repeated.

The first, and best, sensation when the menopause is finished is that the woman has reached a plateau of constancy. She can depend on her moods, which won't fluctuate unduly. She can depend on her body and her energy to be faithful.

With this goes a sense of rebirth and exhilaration beyond description. Now that the fear of an unwanted pregnancy is past, many women find themselves enjoying sexual relations with their husbands for the first time in their lives. I've met women in their fifties as giddy and blushing as newlyweds, and with good reason.

When her menopause is over, a woman has put behind her some of the frustrations that made her thirties and forties an agony. If she is unmarried, she has reached the point where she can finally accept the realization that she will be unmarried all her life. The childless woman, who has run from doctor to doctor for twenty years and has fretted and stalled over the decision to adopt a child, can put all thoughts of children behind her. It is now far too late. These are unhappy truths to accept, but there is great peace in the knowledge that the struggle is over.

Keeping up with the Joneses is also over. In the new-found stability there is no need to buy a new hat every season, to have wall-to-wall broadloom, to possess Toulouse-Lautrec lithographs. It was a great moment for me when I reached the age of fifty and could say fearlessly, "I don't like ballet." I no longer have to pretend.

So I say, if you're starting your menopause, relax. You aren't going to be the same kind of person you have been for the next few years. You're going to have bad days, blue days, confused days and royal flushes. You are going to be difficult to get along with. But as time goes on, the bad days will get further and further apart and eventually they'll stop.

The change—if that's what you're determined to call it—begins at forty-five but, believe me, life begins at fifty.

CHAPTER ELEVEN

Old Age

~~~~~~

A wandering seer once wrote these lines:

> Grow old along with me!
> The best is yet to be,
> The last of life, for which the first was made.

I WANT to make some observations now on old age, the golden years which so many dread and detest. I have seen hundreds of women in open rebellion against aging and I have been astounded by their attitude. No time of life seems to me more rich and blessed than those years after sixty.

In our society, unlike some that are more dignified and gentle, people facing old age are filled with fear. Sometimes they are careful to keep their fright submerged, a stoic tendency that has the power to erode mind and body. Partly they fear oncoming frailties; they also cringe from what seems the looming possibility of being unnecessary and unloved. They are clutched by panic that warps their every attitude.

Because they dread loneliness, some older people complain bitterly at a casual desertion for a few hours. Because they fear uselessness, some cling to the routines of their younger days and are sickened to find themselves poor in strength and energy. Because they want to be loved so desperately, some old people are capable of venomous jealousy.

It is impossible to win a fight against old age. It's hopeless to try to gain the affection and respect of children by insisting on it. It's incompatible with nature for the elderly to perform the duties and functions of the young.

This is the first lesson for all of us, for we are all growing old: Acceptance. It's self-destroying play-acting to struggle against aging, and an enchanting victory to give in with good humor.

Much of aging seems to me highly comic. I'd love to see Cornelia Otis Skinner do a skit about an old woman's preparations for bed—the fussy folding of garments, the creams, lotions, and hair net, the chin strap for sagging neck muscles, the earplugs to keep out noise, the mask to keep out light, the furtive removal of dentures, the deep sigh when it is all done. And old men have a ritual too, just as fastidious and unchanging.

Most people tend to resent with an emotion akin to agony the first symptoms of age. Men are anguished about their hairlines and women weep over wrinkles. I remember the pang I felt the first time I realized that I would need glasses in the operating room. I've scolded myself for it ever since; many people are born with poor eyesight and I count myself fortunate to have had perfect vision for more than forty years.

Old age is full of disabilities that are as much a part of its personality as gray hair. Older people might look forward to the mature delight, now that the children are gone and business responsibilities are lighter, of sleeping late in the mornings. This small leisure has seemed a major advantage of age since the person started getting up in the morning for school—but it doesn't happen. Older people who stay in bed in the morning usually pay for it with a backache.

Backaches aren't the only mishaps. Old people travel

with a load of pills and potions that would have equipped an old-time medicine man. Various parts of their interiors need constant persuasion in order to work properly, and their limbs are full of twinges. Their knees creak a bit when they move and their hands are likely to be shaky in the morning, with a trace of rheumatism.

None of these is worthy of the continuous attention some people pay them. The minor infirmities of aging are natural consequences of living past middle years and should be accepted with the same grace that one accepts the frailties of a beloved friend. The main stream of life shouldn't be dammed with fruitless complainings over trivial discomforts. Let pills and electric blankets work their wonders and get on with living.

Of all the complaints that I have heard from aging women, the loss of their physical beauty makes the least sense. The physical beauty they regret, of course, is the freshness and loveliness of a twenty-year-old. This is a fine form of feminine beauty all right but I don't agree that it is the best. Ask any photographer which face is the better to photograph, the smooth unlined blankness of a girl or the wise, crinkled face of a woman. Television viewers know that young faces are sweet to watch, but forgettable. The lined face of an Eleanor Roosevelt is fascinating, and unforgettable.

I'm truly sorry for a woman who has the misfortune to look younger than her years. If she happens to look about forty-five when she is sixty, she somehow feels challenged to behave like a younger woman. I have some patients who fit this description. They keep themselves in a social madhouse of teas, cocktail parties, dinners, and after-theater receptions. In the end they are defeated by their own lack of stamina, which isn't fooled for an instant about their real age.

Most women approaching sixty these days have better figures than did their mothers at the same age. The current concentration on slenderness has kept thousands of women from the pillow-breasted corset-bursting silhouettes that used to be common. Women shouldn't give up physical activities of which they have been fond —golfing, swimming, skating—merely because they have a nagging feeling that they're getting "too old." Subject to their doctor's approval, they should continue to be active. One patient of mine observed her sixty-first birthday by asking my permission for her to take modern-dance classes. The balletlike movements are keeping her body supple, and her example has attracted several other grandmothers. Some women who have suffered from a lack of vitality and low blood pressure find themselves enjoying their best years.

Since I have reached a time when I am caring for two generations of women (and starting on my third), I often hear my thirty-year-olds complaining that their mothers can work rings around them. "She's sixty years old!" they wail. "We go shopping together and I just can't keep up!"

Of course the older woman has the advantage over her daughter. She's past the strain of a cyclic life with its violent contrasts every month, and she isn't in the middle of the sucking whirlpool known as the modern spirit of competition. Besides this, she's a spectator to the raising of her grandchildren and takes no part in the tedium of teaching table manners and the reason for telling the truth. The woman of sixty is floating along with perfect freedom in what M. Voltaire once called "the best of all possible worlds."

During the sixties one final major decision must be made: What to do on retirement? I'm aghast how often this seems to occur to people on the night before the office farewell party. It's a problem that everyone, and particularly single women, should solve twenty years before it happens. To prevent the sweeping sense of being suddenly cut adrift, a busy and intriguing program

131

should be planned well in advance and timed to start the moment the first pension check arrives.

Here is an area where women are defeated by their own hope. In offices where the pension plan is not compulsory, very few women are interested in joining. To do so would be a shameful admission that they are permanently "old maids," so they avoid being pensioned with a false and ruinous pride.

Even women who have joined pension plans, or whose husbands will receive regular pensions, should also establish systematic savings through their middle years to augment the pension.

The first human necessity for a pensioned person is a home to cherish. The single woman should never live in some dingy room; she needs through her lifetime a comfortable charming haven where she can renew her courage. As she grows older, the need for a home grows with her. It's a good idea to find two or three congenial women of her own age to share a co-operative venture. There doesn't have to be any particular affection for one another—good manners and fundamental interdependency will be sufficient. Separately, aging single women cannot support the expense of a pleasant home. There are other mutual needs, such as the necessity for kindness in case of illness or sadness.

Some people nearing retirement must look deep into themselves to discover where they truly want to end their days. Many of us are not city folk at all but have secretly longed for years to go back to the farm or village of our childhood.

A favorite patient of mine came to me shortly after her fifty-sixth birthday with such a look of glory on her face that I was sure she was in love. "I've found a place of my own," she confided with shining eyes. "My brother has a cabin on his farm that overlooks a stream and a woods. I'm living there weekends now and fixing it up, and when I retire that's where I'm going. I've just discovered that's where I've wanted to be all my life."

Another working woman of my acquaintance spent a good deal of her income for many years winterizing a cottage and filling it with the warmth of copper and chintz. She plans to retire to this bower and she can hardly wait.

Retirement, I feel, means a new adventure in living—not a stopping.

It is time, when people reach their sixties, to give up the strain of a heavy, complex occupation and substitute a new, lighter activity. For women, volunteer work can be perfection. There are hundreds of jobs for capable, knowing hands and the patience and experience of an older woman.

A neighbor of mine discovered the very best job of all. She was a widow and I was sure she would be lonely when her last child was married and moved away. I determined to make an effort to visit her, and I did. But I could never find her at home. She is baby sitting every weekend to give young parents a chance to get away by themselves. She's one of the most valuable people in our community, performing a real service and doing a land-office business.

It is easier for a woman to retire than for a man. Women are the homemakers and this faculty never leaves them. They tend a home throughout their working years and continue on afterward without a break. When a man retires it is as if the main switch of his life is turned off and he stands empty-handed. His concentration on success has excluded all other interests, sometimes even his family. He has no resources and he collapses with retirement, ages every day, and wills himself to die.

This is a tragic circumstance but one that is all too common. Retirement needs planning, and wives should prevent their husbands from indulging in the fantasy that they will never be sixty-five. Some men can turn happily to gardens and I know one ulcer-ridden executive who discovered that he was a fine carpenter and has filled his children's homes with tables and bookcases they couldn't afford to buy. Such men wear leisure becomingly and look younger with the passing years.

Most men facing retirement should find a job that doesn't involve the physical endurance and nervous frustration better carried by younger men. This means a job with less responsibility, which many men foolishly consider insulting. It is humiliating for a human to feel less valuable, but such feelings are illogical in an older man. Let the young men carry the weight of decisions now and be content to be a counselor, keeping in mind that it's a healthy sign of independence for the young to ignore the advice of elder statesmen. The older man's contribution to society is his experience—not his vigor.

The years of retirement are sometimes blessed with the beginning of a marriage that has suffered from abuse, ennui, and irritation for many decades. In the fine, quiet years of old age, the man and wife learn companionship and affection for perhaps the first time. Drawn together by their common interest in the progress of their children, they find new value in their union. As they break down a little in vitality and health—the husband with his touch of gout and the wife with her rheumatism—they become gentle in mutual sympathy.

This is a sad time for broken marriages because almost certainly the wife will be rejoicing in her grandchildren while the husband is alone and possibly unwelcome.

I learned during the war that grandmothers are the solid framework on which the world rests. I was delivering as many as five babies in a day and I usually found the waiting room filled with women. The men were away, fighting a war, but the grandmothers were standing by their daughters. Just a few months ago the husband of a patient of mine was killed in an auto accident

134

just before her baby was born. When I finished the delivery and came into the hospital corridor to give the news to the family, there was the grandmother again, solid and sure.

One result of grandmothers standing by unfortunately can be that the older woman moves right in with her daughter or son. There are exceptions, but this is usually an unhappy arrangement. The main difficulty is that the roles of the two women involved are reversed and neither can adjust. The daughter is in charge of the household, where once she was an inept pupil in household arts leaning on her mother's counsel. The mother is a guest whose advice breeds antagonism, where once she was queen of all she surveyed.

It is a bitter dose for anyone to become dependent. Even brides find it awkward to accept money from their husbands at first, an embarrassment that sometimes takes years to dissipate. Consider how much more galling it is for an older person, accustomed to his own home and his own well-earned income for forty years, to move in with young people whose routine is unfamiliar and be forced to need from them gifts of food, clothes, cigarettes, and affection. It is too much to bear, and the young couple shouldn't be surprised to find, instead of the gentle, grateful citizen they expected, an irascible, agitated old person. It would be flying in the face of human nature to behave otherwise.

Many young people, moved by the violent emotion that follows a death in the family, urge the remaining parent to join their household. *Don't* be hasty. I say this for the sake of the older person. No one should remove an aging person's independence from him without realizing that there is a risk of blighting that person's existence. The older man or woman is far better off with fewer material advantages in a place where independence of behavior is possible than in the most elegant room in a home where conformity with local rules is required.

Ideally, the housing found for older people should be close to their younger relatives, so that visiting can be frequent. Many older people, particularly the cranky ones, are best off in a senior citizens' home, where they can happily argue all day long with their contemporaries. I'm discouraged at the number of people who prefer the misery of living with a bad-tempered old person to the pleasant solution of supporting him or her in an old people's home.

"How can I have such a thing on my conscience?" they protest. "I can't send my mother away!"

Nonsense. Put it on a trial basis and see if I'm not right. Providing the family ties are not dissolved by the separation, the older person will thrive in the company of other elderly people.

If, however, there is no alternative to the older person moving in, a set of firm rules should be established in the beginning. Later on it will be impossible to set up any restrictions without tears on the one hand and guilt on the other.

The needs of every household will differ, but I think it is essential that the main part of the family should have breakfast alone. The mother can get a good start on her day and the husband and children set off for work and school peacefully, without the germ of irritation that fuses the bomb of temper.

This can be accomplished by having the older person wait until later for breakfast or by taking the meal to his room on a tray.

An agreement on which television programs will be watched needs to be reached, because the tastes are certain to differ. All the problems of raising children should be strictly off limits to older people. Some older people try to dominate and influence a home, because they are accustomed to power, and this must not be allowed to happen or else the home will deteriorate.

Younger people must be prepared to accept with good grace the disadvantages that adhere to old people. Some have distressing habits, such as coughing, wandering around the house at dawn, leaving their teeth in conspicuous places. Others have no use for the benefits of an easy silence, but want to chatter continuously. None of these habits can be changed. In addition older people should not be harassed by the constant need to be grateful to the young; gratitude is an odious burden.

Establish some workable arrangement, keeping in mind that it can never be perfect. Old people can be assigned certain chores that will be their special responsibility and remove them from the younger person's direction. The younger woman usually prefers to run her kitchen alone, and this should be made clear at the beginning.

If their health permits, older people can find some part-time activity such as a charitable organization or advising a young business, and keep in touch with contemporaries socially. The most difficult situation is the one where the older person isn't well enough to leave the home but is well enough not to be bedridden. The family never functions by itself.

In all cases where a home is being shared with aging parents, the younger couple must have a vacation separately. The wife especially needs relief from the mental strain and physical fatigue of such an arrangement. This is vital to renew her endurance. A yearly itinerary of family visits is ideal and should be begun at once.

Understand this: Old people, most of them, are full of complaints. This is as natural a part of their psychology as arguments are to children. It's a form of attention-getting and should be treated mellowly, particularly by visiting members of the family. The older person can remember when he was healthy, sturdy, busy, and needed; his present existence cannot possibly look as good.

Disabilities, both mental and physical, vary greatly both in the age of onset and the speed with which they increase. For many old persons there comes a time when they must be cared for in a convalescent hospital or nursing home. Face this situation in time and with realistic insight. If nursing care and safety precautions are necessary, never hesitate to take them to an institution properly equipped to give it. They will be happier and more content. When the memory is gone but the mind is still active, be willing to risk on the safety side to preserve a little independence for the older one. Never hesitate to try a short period in an institution to give the family a chance to take stock again. You may find to your astonishment that everyone is happier when the dear Old One comes home again. The life of the family has centered around this gentle needful creature, and draws strength from its service.

Younger people must reassure their elders that they are still needed, as indeed they are. Old people give their grandchildren the sense of constancy of family and race that makes the ground firm under their feet. An old woman with her grandchild is beautiful to see. I remember my mother with my three-year-old niece at her knee. They were content to sit like that without words; the old woman moved slowly and the little girl couldn't express herself very well, but they had a communion. I know of a grandfather in another neighborhood who teaches the children in his area to recognize and value birds. No one else has the time and the patience, but he has both.

There is a saying that the good die young. It means that the good are always young in spirit, no matter when they die. Old people must have this young spirit, the kind of outlook that delights in the new day and its gifts—friends, laughter, flowers, a yellow leaf, fresh snowfall. The struggle and confusion of being young are over and the moments of great gaiety and triumph are gone too. Memories are left and the wisdom that can only come with many defeats and victories.

Old age is a time to be gentle and serene. Such composure can only come from a deep faith that steadies courage. Old people need to believe in immortality, and why not? They leave warmth with the little people, and kindness; leave understanding and humor; leave assurance that growing old is a happy experience, not a bitterness; leave a sense of peace and radiance.

They will live forever, for they will never be forgotten.

CHAPTER TWELVE

The Key Is Faith

A FEW months ago a group of the women doctors who direct Women's College Hospital in Toronto were having a party in honor of a younger group just added to the staff. We stood aside as the juniors swapped spirited shoptalk, challenged one another's opinions, and giggled like girls in the midst of some complicated medical theorizing. The chief of our hospital chuckled fondly at them. "In ten years, girls, you'll be running this hospital."

One young doctor looked up sharply. She's an endocrinal specialist, working on grant-supported radium research and so brilliant that I am both awed and delighted by her. "Nonsense." She grinned at the row of us, gray-haired and middle-aged. "We'll be running your hospital in five years."

I wouldn't be at all surprised. I retire this spring as

Chief of Obstetrics and Gynecology. I've been packing up my private practice gradually over the past three years, passing it along to younger women of miraculous competence and confidence. I watched one of them deliver a baby only a few days ago. She's a Japanese-Canadian, small and fragile and possessed of magnificent sensitivity in a delivery room. I felt choked by strong emotion in that moment, and movement in the room seemed to stop, as in a tableau. I knew a giddy pride in my profession, in my sex, and in myself. There was a blessedness in the room—the woman on the delivery table with the beginning of glory in her face, the tiny doctor holding the new infant with skill and affection, the first, raw sound of a cry. I thought of my twenty-five years in this room and others like it, less well equipped. I stood tall and felt strong because I have done my work well enough so that I am no longer needed, and because I am comfortable with my no-longer-young body and my conscience treats me benignly.

I'm ready now to live some dreams I've been keeping in reserve for my retirement. I want to help the pioneer work of women doctors in hospitals in India and China. I hope to live a year or so in Greece or Turkey, where women doctors are involved in exciting pioneering. I want to hear opera in Milan and go salmon fishing in British Columbia. Now that I am fifty-five, I can scarcely wait to get at the future.

One of the final acts of my professional career in Toronto was an address I made to the graduating class in nursing. I decided to attempt to sort out for them my philosophy of life. I found some empty hours one afternoon when a soft spring wind was blowing through my garden, which crowns a cliff on a dizzy height above Lake Ontario. I sat still and considered my beliefs.

First, I realized, I have no faith in the fairness of life. There is no balance of reward for effort or happiness for a kind heart. There is rarely even gratitude. No one can expect that life will be gracious and filled with esteem for the mere reason of worthiness. You don't get out of living what you deserve. Since it is impossible for even the most saintly to live without misfortune, the hope for the serene survival of the spirit is in acceptance.

I don't mean the passive, heavy acceptance called fatalism. This is far too inert for me. I believe that living is too important, too highly charged with potential, to be derailed by a brutal kick from fate. There's laughter going on, and hard work, and occasional rockets of worthwhile achievement slashing the darkness. The immobility of self-pity is a kind of death, a suicide.

I believe in timing. It is crystallized for me in the moment of greatness that an athlete like Mickey Mantle knows for that fraction of time when his bat meets the ball squarely and sends it out of the park. This is true timing—the health and animal instinct of a superb athlete performing perfectly at the time and place best suited to him.

All individuals must find this kind of timing. In that lovely movie *Lili,* the girl says, "There is a time for growing up, there is a time for going to school, there is a time for falling in love." This timing process can't be rushed or the whole pattern of a life is jostled. It must be taken with fluid grace, one step at a time. This is the beginning of wisdom.

Timing has its own rhythm. In each life there is a time, clearly defined by nature in the extra vigor of the young, for striving and ambition; there is an ebb time for tranquillity. There is a time for passion and a time for contentment. The reckless ones who try to jar the rhythm and look for peace when it is too soon or accomplishment when it is too late can only be shattered.

Life holds one certain quality for everyone—suffering.

141

This is to be expected. The extra bonus that life sometimes gives is achievement. I would never wish anyone a life of prosperity and security. These are bound to betray. I would wish instead for adventure, struggle, and challenge. These have one benefit in common—they require a pinnacle of effort, the very best. Nothing in life is as glorious as reaching beyond capacity.

Challenge is especially good for the soul. I was always amused to notice, on gloriously fine days, how many of my obstetrical patients forgot their appointments entirely. On wild, winter days with a slanting sleet storm and treacherous footing, I would find them all present, faces shining with glee because they had braved the hazards.

I once saw two pictures in the same magazine of athletes who were attracting attention. One athlete was Johnny Podres and he had just finished pitching the Dodgers to a World Series victory. The other athlete was captain of a basketball team—that played from wheel chairs. To me there is no question which is the better athlete—the man who wins a World Series game or the man who plays basketball from a wheel chair. I haven't a doubt either about which one has the greater likelihood of adjusting to life.

I think the key word in this, underlying acceptance and timing, is faith. I found the best example of what I mean in a sculpture by Michelangelo that stands in St. Peter's in Rome. I stood before it and wept. It is a young and beautiful girl, holding in her arms the broken body of her child. The curve of her body expresses her acceptance of this agony, and her unlined face glows with faith.

Faith is the antidote for wretchedness and loneliness, the only one. I care so much what people put their faith in. It must be a spiritual force greater than themselves. With faith comes the ability to love, the greatest treasure of them all. If you are able to love, you will be loved. It's like breathing in and breathing out, a simple spiritual law. You can't buy it, you can't demand it, and you can't even expect it. You must give love, without being afraid, in order to receive it. Love once given never disappears.

Sitting in the sunlight that afternoon, I thought of these things and knew them to be right. I remembered the misery of my childlessness that used to be so familiar, and the other less bitter renunciations I have known. The pangs are faint now, but I have the understanding that comes with knowing them.

I'm starting a new life soon. Wish something with me. Wish that it will be difficult. And full of laughter.

Index

144

INDEX

ACCLAIM — from Critics, Counselors and Doctors

▶"A sound discussion of women's problems . . . the best in the field that I have read."

—*Ladies' Home Journal*

▶"It answers most of the asked and unasked questions in any female patient's mind."

—VERNELLE FOX, M.D.

▶"Discusses love and marriage with sound good sense . . ."

—*Fort Worth Press*

▶"Valuable . . . sensible . . . sympathetic . . . her theory of fatigue is of special significance to the woman who just never feels really rested or caught up."

—*Charm*

▶"The author writes with a sensitive insight and a warm understanding of her material which is conveyed to the reader in an intimate, simple manner."

—ELIZABETH HAUSER, M.D.

▶"It tells so much that no reader should be disappointed—woman or man."

—AMERICAN INSTITUTE OF FAMILY RELATIONS

▶"If every bride were required to read this sensible, entertaining book, we feel sure there would be fewer unhappy women in the world—with all that implies."

—*Hartford Times*